Introductory
Statistics

C000120587

Stafford College

STAFFORD COLLEGE
CENTRAL
LEARNING
SERVICES

WITHDRAWN FROM THE LIBRARY

23-08

Introductory Statistics

A. M. Plews, M.A., F.S.S.
Formerly Lecturer in Mathematics and Statistics,
Barnet College, London

HEINEMANN
EDUCATIONAL

WITHDRAWN FROM THE LIBRARY

HR 8.95

Heinemann Educational a division of
Heinemann Education Books Ltd,
Halley Court, Jordan Hill, Oxford OX2 8EJ

OXFORD   LONDON   EDINBURGH   MADRID
ATHENS   BOLOGNA   PARIS   MELBOURNE
SYDNEY   AUCKLAND   SINGAPORE   TOKYO
IBADAN   NAIROBI   HARARE   GABORONE
PORTSMOUTH NH (USA)

STAFFORD
COLLEGE
C.L.S

DON

ACCESSION No.

32209

CLASS No.

TL
519.2

To Peg, without whom . . . .

ISBN 0 435 53750 4

© A. M. Plews 1979

First published 1979
92 93 94 95 17 16 15 14 13 12 11 10 9

British Library Cataloguing in Publication Data

Plews, A. M.
  Introductory statistics
  I. Mathematical statistics
  I. Title
  519.5   QA276
  ISBN 0-435-53750-4

Printed and bound in Great Britain by
Athenaeum Press Ltd, Newcastle upon Tyne.

Preface

Statistics are like alienists – they will testify for either side.
F.H. La Guardia

For some years I have been aware of a growing demand for a textbook that would be suitable for those studying Statistics for the first time, particularly students contemplating taking various 'O' Level examinations, either in statistics as such or in other subjects where statistics is also required. Unfortunately, there appears to be a dearth of suitable books which can be recommended, although there are a variety of books, each of which is partly relevant. This situation is clearly unsatisfactory and the purpose here is to present, in a single book, all that is required to enable a student to cover the subject up to 'O' Level standard.

In particular, the book covers the syllabuses for the following: 'O' Level Statistics for the Associated Examining Board (A.E.B.), the Welsh Joint Education Committee (W.J.E.C.), and the West African Examinations Council (W.A.E.C.); O Grade Statistics for the Scottish Certificate of Education Examinations Board (S.C.E); the Statistics sections of 'O' Level Mathematics (Syllabus C), 'O' Level Commercial Mathematics, and 'O' Level Additional Mathematics (Pure Mathematics with Statistics) for the Joint Matriculation Board (J.M.B); and for Northern Ireland (N.I.), the Statistics section of 'O' Level Additional Mathematics. The book also covers substantial portions of other 'O' Level and Alternative 'O' Level syllabuses. I am particularly indebted to these Examining bodies and the following for permission to reproduce their questions—these form an essential part of the book: London University (L.U.), Oxford and Cambridge (O. & C.), Cambridge University (C.U.).

I should like to take this opportunity to thank three people who greatly helped during the writing of this book. Firstly, my wife Peggy who helped perform many of the wearisome chores associated with a project of this kind, and whose help and encouragement were always an inspiration. Secondly, Maureen Larman, who somehow or other managed to decipher my appalling handwriting, and who typed out the final manuscript, and thirdly Deborah Ganz for her help in getting the book to press.

Finally, it has to be realized that Statistics is a dichotomy, that is, the subject comprises not only *descriptive* statistics but also *mathematical* statistics, and this is bound to present any would-be writer with a dilemma: how to adequately cover *both* aspects in a *single* book. I have tried to do just this, but nevertheless, I am well aware that I am probably attempting the impossible. I would, therefore, be very grateful for any comments that teachers, students or others may have on the book.

1979   A.M.P.

Contents

1
The collection of statistical data

Introduction

What do we mean by Statistics? It is just as well to have some kind of a definition in mind before embarking on the subject. The trouble is that if we went to several different statisticians they would probably each give us a slightly different answer!

For our purposes, it is probably sufficient if we think of Statistics as being that science which concerns itself with data coming from ourselves and from our environment (both natural and man-made), and which seeks to mould that data, by various means, into a form from which we can derive useful and necessary information. The purpose of this book is to explain how, in practice, this can be done.

1.1   Census

Before we can extract useful and necessary information from statistical data, we have to collect it. How are we to do this? In fact, we can go about it in a number of ways. If, for instance, we wanted to know the average height of all 14 year-old boys in a certain town, we *could* go and ask every single boy falling into that category to tell us his height. This would, of course, be an extremely tedious and time-consuming job, for we would be conducting what is called a *census*. In a census every single member of the *population* (in this case, all 14 year-old boys in a certain town) is examined and the value of the particular *variable* (here, the height of the boys) that we are interested in is noted for each member.

The advantage of a census is that it should give us a completely accurate result. Its disadvantages, however, are grave: it is tedious, time-consuming, and costly. The question therefore arises as to whether there is some way in which we can still obtain useful information about a particular population without having to examine every individual member. This leads us naturally on to the second topic in this chapter, namely *sampling*.

1.2   Sampling

Consider, as before, the problem of estimating the average height of those 14 year-old boys. Let us assume, for the sake of simplicity, that there are 700 of them. For the reasons already mentioned, we do not want to examine anywhere near this number. Is there some way in which we could select say a *sample* of 70 boys, measure their heights, and still obtain a good estimate for the average height of them all? The answer, fortunately, is yes! In fact, it can be argued that it was precisely because of this type of problem that the science of statistics evolved. For, provided we choose our sample with great care, we can make a good estimate of the average height, despite having looked at only a 10 per cent sample of the total population. Moreover, we shall have saved a tremendous amount of time and effort. Let us now look at the various ways of obtaining a *representative sample* from a population.

1.2.1   *Random sampling*

This is probably the commonest and in many cases by far the best type of sample to extract from a population. We proceed as follows: taking as our population the 700 boys mentioned above, and assuming we have a list of their names (we do *not* need to have them in any particular order), we firstly number these from 1 to 700. Now, since the later members of our population in this particular case will have three-digit numbers, we have to number the earlier members as if they also were three-digit numbers, i.e. we number them 001, 002, ..., 009, 010, 011, ..., 099, 100, 101, ..., 700. The reason we do this is because to obtain a *random sample* we generally make use of *Tables of Random Sampling Numbers*. These tables are extremely useful to a statistician and they often comprise 2000 or more digits. By 'digit' we mean any of the first ten integers starting with 0, i.e. 0, 1, 2, 3, 4, 5, 6, 7, 8 or 9. In every single case the digit selected is equally likely to be any one of these values. Another way of putting it is to say that in every single case the *probability* of a particular digit being selected is $\frac{1}{10}$, so that all ten digits always have the same chance of being selected *no matter how many times they may have already been included.*

Nowadays, computers can be used to provide us with these tables, making use of the completely random behaviour of electrons under carefully controlled conditions. (The apparatus known as 'ERNIE', which selects the winning Premium Bond numbers, is in fact a device of this type. The name 'ERNIE' is an acronym derived from Electronic Random Number Indicator Equipment.) We can therefore be sure that our tables of digits are truly random, hence their title.

An example of such tables are those compiled by D.V. Lindley and J.C.P. Miller in their book *Cambridge Elementary Statistical Tables*, published by Cambridge University Press. The first two extreme left-hand columns of their tables commence with the following digits:

20	17	42	28
74	49	04	49
94	70	49	31
22	15	78	15
93	29	12	18
45	04	77	97
44	91	99	49
16	23	91	02
04	50	65	04
32	70	17	72

Now, to obtain our *sample* of size 70, we merely require 70 random numbers lying between 001 and 700 inclusive, in order to know which members of our numbered population to select. Using the above tables as an illustration, one way of doing this would be as follows:

20	1 ¦ 7	
74	4 ¦ 9	
94	7 ¦ 0	
22	1 ¦ 5	
93	2 ¦ 9	
45	0 ¦ 4	
44	9 ¦ 1	
16	2 ¦ 3	
04	5 ¦ 0	
32	7 ¦ 0 etc.	

Imagine that a broken vertical line is drawn in on the table as shown above, to give us a vertical set of three-digit numbers. Now, reading down from the top, and ignoring irrelevant numbers such as 744, 947, etc. which exceed our total population, we obtain: 201, 221, 450, 449, 162, 045, 327, ..., etc. We continue in this manner until we have a set of 70 numbers lying between 1 and 700.

We now go to our original population and construct our sample by selecting from it the 201st member, the 221st member, the 450th member, and so on.

1.2.2   *Systematic sampling*

As its name implies, this method involves a system – the system in this case being one of regularity. We proceed as follows, still taking as our example of a population the heights of all 14 year-old boys in a certain town.

We begin with a list of the names of the 700 boys, from which we require a representative sample of 70. Now, 700 divided by 70 equals 10. Accordingly, we go through our list and select every 10th name. Precisely where we start is immaterial, provided that once we have decided we keep to the above rule. For example, we would probably tend to select the first name and, having done this, we would then take the 11th, 21st, 31st, and so on until we took as our final name the 691st. But we could just as validly select the 2nd, 12th, 22nd, etc., names and finish up with a sample of the required type.

Now, remember that the whole crux of the matter, if we are going to use a *sample* rather than a *population* to estimate our average value, is that *every member of the population should have an equal chance of selection*, in order that the sample should be a truly representative one. In other words, we must try and avoid, at all costs, getting a biased sample. In general, it is unlikely that a list of names would be biased in any way and so our sample should be a satisfactory one.

To sum up the general method: we take our *population* of size N (which could be heights of 14 year-old boys, lengths of a particular type of nail, marks of candidates in a certain examination, etc.); we number each member of the population from 1 to N; then, if we require a *sample* of size n, we select every (N/n)th member.

1.2.3 *Stratified sampling (or proportional sampling)*

It has already been stressed how important it is, if we are to work with *samples* rather than *populations*, for our sample to be truly representative.

Consider the following hypothetical case: suppose we wish to estimate the average weight of all people over 18 years old living in Britain. Suppose further that we *know* that in this particular population the percentage of men is 45 and that the percentage of women is therefore 55. We have decided (for one reason or another) that we require a sample of size 3000. Now we could *not* make use of either random or systematic sampling without introducing an important constraint, i.e., since our *population* comprises 45 per cent men : 55 per cent women, it is normally desirable that our *sample* should also reflect this situation. Therefore, we must ensure that out of our sample of 3000, 45 per cent of the 3000 members should be men (= 1350) and 55 per cent women (= 1650). We could then use either a random or systematic sample, going through our list *twice* so as to obtain 1350 men and 1650 women. In this example we would have constructed what statisticians call a *stratified sample*. Whenever our population naturally subdivides itself into a number of *sub-populations* or *strata*, we must exercise particular care in how we obtain our *sample*. Often this involves using the above method.

1.2.4 *Quota sampling*

Quota sampling, as its name suggests, brings in the constraint of *quotas*, that is to say, the particular person, whose task it is to compile the sample, is given a series of quotas – thus he or she may be instructed to interview as many men as women, as many adults as children, as many young people as old people, equal numbers from the four or five generally recognized social classes, and so on. This series of quotas obviously imposes a severe constraint on the sampler, and rightly so for, of course, the idea is to obtain a sample of the total population which is as truly representative as possible. Nevertheless the sampler still has far more freedom than if instructed to obtain say a random or systematic sample, where specified individuals must be seen, and consequently there is always the danger that subjective judgements will creep in making the sample less random than is desirable. For this reason quota samples, although frequently used by opinion-gathering agencies of various kinds, are often criticised by statisticians and others.

1.2.5 *Cluster sampling*

If the particular population from which we are sampling naturally sub-divides into a number of small *homogeneous* groups or *clusters*, then it can be convenient in such a case to take an appropriate selection of these and, having done so, *examine every member* of each cluster. When we decide to construct our sample in this way we are said to be *cluster sampling*.

A simple example, where cluster sampling could be used, would be if we were interested in say family expenditure, when we could use as our clusters the various family households. In other cases our clusters might be generated on a geographical basis, and so on.

1.3 Pilot Surveys

Let us return for a moment to the subject of the census (section 1.1). Many readers will probably remember the April 1981 Census conducted by the British Government (even if they did not have to provide any information for it themselves). In this Census, every known householder in Great Britain received a *census form* which, by law, they were required to complete and return to an appointed official by a certain date. The form was a complicated one and contained detailed instructions on how to complete the various sections. A particularly important piece of information that had to be supplied by the householder was the name of every single member of that household who was present for the night of April 25/26. This was to ensure that the Government would be able to get an extremely accurate population count for that particular date. (By its nature, no census of this kind can ever be 100 per cent accurate – some people would be out of the country for instance, a few would refuse to complete the forms, and so on.)

Every government *needs* to conduct a census from time to time, because the accurate population counts they provide enable them to plan *sensibly* in the matter of, for instance, house building, schools programmes, new hospitals, the desirability or otherwise of extending motorway networks, etc.

In Britain a full census is normally conducted every ten years and it yields such an avalanche of information that, before the advent of the computer, by the time all the information had been analysed, it was practically time for the next census! The coming of computers has changed all this, and the Government has already been provided with much useful information from the 1981 Census almost entirely due to the capability of a modern computer (suitably programmed) to ingest, analyse, and tabulate vast quantities of statistics in a fraction of the time that a whole army of statisticians would take.

Bearing in mind the importance of a census, therefore, and its obvious cost in both money and manpower, no government is going to send out say fifteen million census forms, until it is absolutely satisfied that the forms have been drafted in such a way that the vast majority of the people will be able to fill them in without undue difficulty (the small minority who could not complete the April 1981 form themselves, were helped to do so by sympathetic and helpful officials).

Accordingly, some time before the full census is taken, the Government operates what is in effect a 'dummy run'. A Proposed Form is sent out to a small representative sample of the population, who are asked to complete it and also to state whether they found any questions difficult to understand or ambiguous. In this way, amendments to the Proposed Form (if any), can be made *before* the full census. 'Dummy runs' of the kind just described are known as *pilot surveys*. As has already been stressed several times, the 'art' involved in the 'science' of statistics is to get away from *populations* and into *samples*. But when complete accuracy is required a *census* is unavoidable. In this case *pilot surveys* have an absolutely vital part to play. They must precede the full census and they have to be undertaken for the reasons already given. In addition, it is perhaps worth mentioning that few people are going to take kindly to being asked, *having already filled in one census form*, to disregard this and fill in an amended form a short time later. (The Author found that it took him about two hours to complete the 1981 form; most of us can think of pleasanter ways of spending such a period!)

1.4　Questionnaires

A census form is an example of a rather specialized type of *questionnaire*, so in a sense this topic has already been touched upon, although not by name. What, then, is a questionnaire? What is its purpose? How should it be drafted? The purpose of this section is to try and answer these questions.

1.4.1　*Definition of a questionnaire*
Statistics is *not* an exact science and it is pointless trying to come up with a definition that will please everyone. For our purposes we may define a *questionnaire* as a kind of statistical form, containing *questions* which we wish to have answered. The questionnaire will sometimes be completed for the interviewee (or *respondent*) by a trained interviewer, who in this case would not normally allow the actual questionnaire to be seen, but quite often it will be completed by the respondent himself, who in this case would clearly need to see it.

1.4.2　*The purpose of a questionnaire*
We have already stated that a questionnaire contains questions, and naturally enough we hope to have these questions answered, because as statisticians we are hoping to elicit useful information, which at a later time we can analyse. We can think of a questionnaire, therefore, as one method of collecting statistical data.

1.4.3　*The drafting of a questionnaire*
A whole book could be written on this topic alone! Unfortunately, we haven't the time to do this, nor indeed is it necessary for the purposes of this book.

All that will be attempted in this section is a brief discussion of the desirable elements in any questionnaire.

1.   The *purpose* behind the questionnaire should be explained to the respondent (either orally or in writing).

2.   The *questions* themselves should:
  (a) be readily comprehensible to the type of person for whom they are intended;
  (b) be unambiguous (not nearly as simple as it might sound, as anyone who has ever had to draft a questionnaire will confirm);
  (c) be as brief as possible;
  (d) *not* require knowledge which the compiler has no right to expect that particular type of respondent to have;
  (e) not be emotively phrased;
  (f) not try to influence the respondent into giving a particular or desired answer;
  (g) not give the respondent an 'easy' option; and
  (h) wherever possible, require either 'yes/no' responses, or be framed in such a manner that one of a number of alternative answers, *present on the form*, may be ticked. When the answers to a question can be classified as, for example, 'yes', 'no' or 'don't know', the question is said to be *closed-ended*; in contrast, questions calling for an opinion are generally *open-ended*.

Let us try and elaborate on each of the above 'rules' by giving examples of how *not* to draft questions.

  (a) *Question (addressed to a dispensing chemist)*: 'How many part-time staff you employ are concerned with the sales of photographic materials?' (Incredible though it may seem, the Author has seen a question like this in a real questionnaire!)
  (b) *Question (addressed to any member of the public)*: 'How tall are you?' The reader can probably see just how ambiguous this question really is.
  (c) No example is required here, for a long rambling question is quite self-evident.
  (d) *Question (addressed to a housewife)*: 'Do you think that "deficit budgeting", as practised in the U.S.A., is a system that ought to be adopted in Great Britain?'
  (e) *Question (addressed to any member of the public)*: 'Do you consider that the Government is making a lousy job of controlling rising prices?'
  (f) *Question (addressed to any consumer)*: 'You probably agree, don't you, that Blogg's tomato soup is the best there is?'
  (g) *Question (addressed to any elector)*: 'In the forthcoming General Election will you vote for (i) Party A, (ii) Party B or (iii) are you undecided?' How tempting for the respondent to opt for (iii) if only to get rid of the interviewer!

(h) *Question (addressed to a motorist)*: 'Do you own a Forris 1700 car? If so, describe as clearly as you can its merits as compared with the Vaustin 1900.' Almost inevitably the question exhibits faults (c) as well.

3. The *respondents should be thanked* for their co-operation in completing the questionnaire, if only for the reason that they are more likely to complete it if they are.

4. The respondents should be assured that the information they give will be *strictly confidential*. This is a pledge that *must be honoured*. They must also be assured that their name will not be associated in any way with the particular information they have given.

In the April 1971 Census, in one or two isolated cases only, the pledge given on confidentiality was broken. Nevertheless, it was deplorable and in one particular instance the Commissioners of Inland Revenue failed to obtain payment of income-tax simply because they had learned about the unpaid tax improperly.

N.B.   Very often 1, 3, and 4 will all be combined in a simple explanatory note, preferably at the beginning of the questionnaire before the actual questions.

1.4.4   *Dealing with bias*
Before dealing with this subject, we should try and define what we mean by the term 'bias'.

Bias can basically be considered as leading to 'slanted' statistical information. This does *not* mean to imply that it is always done deliberately. However, human nature being what it is, it would be a bold person indeed who could put his hand on his heart and maintain: 'I have never supplied biased information.'

Bias can generally arise from two sources: it can come from the *respondent* (i.e. the person who, in one way or another, is completing the questionnaire) or it can come from the *interviewer* (if it is the type of questionnaire completed by the interview method). Let us look at these two sources of bias in a little more detail.

1.   *Bias on the part of the interviewer*
This type of bias is generally easier to control than the other. Indeed, careful design of a questionnaire can make it exceedingly difficult, if not impossible, for the interviewer to complete it other than in an impartial way. Of course, it goes without saying that trained interviewers are unlikely, in any case, to be biased.

2.   *Bias on the part of the respondent*
This type of bias is almost impossible to eliminate! We can try and frame our questions very carefully, in order to take into account the fact that some people may deliberately wish to provide us with biased information, and we may even have allowed for the fact that some of the information we receive *will* be

biased. But try as we may, we will never be able to eliminate this type of bias completely.

Most of us, if we are honest with ourselves, will always try to put the best gloss on any information sought. *Nobody* likes admitting that they are poor, or that they live in a slum, or that they smoke 65 cigarettes a day, or that they only read about one book a year, etc. It is quite clear then that some bias is almost inevitable. All that a person framing a questionnaire can hope to do is to seek to reduce the possibility of it as much as he possibly can and to make due allowance for it.

Exercise 1

1. A group of pupils wished to investigate whether there was any correlation between the age and the height of the pupils in their school. To obtain the necessary information they gave each pupil a copy of the following questionnaire:

   ABC School.
   Statistical Investigation–1977

   State your   (i)   Name.........
                (ii) Age.........
                (iii) Height.........

   (a) List the faults of the above questionnaire form.
   (b) Rewrite the questionnaire in a form you consider suitable.

   (A.E.B.)

2. State briefly the main points to be observed in preparing questions for a questionnaire.
   A questionnaire, directed at housewives, was to be issued by a manufacturer of tinned foods and the following items were suggested:
   (a) What is your age?
   (b) Have you any children?
   (c) How much does your husband earn a week?
   (d) Make a list of the tinned foods in your house.
   Comment briefly on the suitability, or otherwise, of each item and make suggestions as to how you think these items could be improved.

   (A.E.B.)

3. Which of the following methods would you use to obtain a representative sample of adults.
   A. Select names from the telephone directory.
   B. Select persons at random from the high street.
   C. Select every tenth name from the Electoral Register.
   D. Select one particular street and use all the residents living there.

   (A.E.B.)

4. A biased sample is one which is
   A. affected by a one-sided influence.
   B. expected to turn up.
   C. rarely expected to turn up.
   D. selected with care.

   (A.E.B.)

5. The questions in a public questionnaire should *not*
   A. be courteously phrased.

    B. require specialist knowledge to answer.

    C. be ambiguous.

    D. require goodwill to answer.

(A.E.B.)

6. What is a random sample?

    A. One consisting of every tenth item.

    B. One affected by a one-sided influence.

    C. One which is always typical of the population.

    D. One where each member of the population has an equal chance of being selected.

(A.E.B)

7. Give briefly three rules to be followed when phrasing questions to be included in a questionnaire.

(A.E.B.)

8. Explain briefly what is meant by a biased sample, and give an example where it might arise.

9. In a co-educational secondary school of approximately 500 pupils, a senior pupil is given permission to produce a school newsheet on a monthly basis, provided there are enough pupils prepared (a) to contribute short articles, news of pupils, etc., (b) to purchase the news-sheet at a nominal price to cover the cost of materials. Draw up a questionnaire, of not more than ten questions, to enable the pupils to decide whether the project is possible.

    If 100 questionnaires are used, how should they be distributed in order to obtain replies representative of the school?

(A.E.B.)

10. Explain clearly the main methods generally used for extracting a sample from a given population. How does the nature of the population itself often determine what type of sampling must be used?

11. A sample comprising 150 members is required from a population comprising 5000 members. It is known that the population falls into three categories made up of: 1500 members in Category A, 3000 members in Category B, and 500 members in Category C. Explain clearly how you would extract a stratified sample of the required size.

12. A population of 300 members has the following values:

10.11	10.05	10.02	9.88	9.99	10.20
10.02	9.89	9.98	9.85	10.15	10.00
10.01	9.96	9.99	9.97	9.98	10.13
10.00	10.02	9.91	10.15	10.00	9.98
10.02	10.00	9.80	10.10	10.02	9.99
9.86	10.04	10.23	9.92	10.05	10.00
9.99	9.96	10.04	9.98	10.01	9.95
10.18	9.96	9.90	10.08	10.12	10.24
9.96	9.87	9.87	9.86	10.09	10.12
10.16	10.11	9.85	9.98	10.05	9.99
9.98	9.89	9.91	9.90	10.03	9.72
9.91	10.02	10.00	9.92	10.15	9.94
9.95	10.09	9.96	10.18	10.21	9.93
10.04	10.01	9.96	10.01	10.08	10.12

9.88	9.93	9.76	10.13	9.74	9.97
10.01	10.16	10.10	9.83	9.99	10.06
9.96	10.02	9.92	9.91	9.83	10.02
9.86	10.01	9.95	10.17	10.07	10.03
9.98	10.02	10.00	9.95	10.04	9.84
9.94	9.95	9.97	9.82	10.10	9.81
10.08	9.96	10.13	9.99	9.90	9.90
10.04	9.87	10.04	9.85	10.04	10.26
9.94	10.14	10.13	9.82	9.98	10.03
9.83	9.89	10.06	9.93	10.09	10.03
9.99	9.96	10.07	10.12	9.95	9.95
9.99	9.95	9.97	9.99	10.03	10.17
9.76	9.75	10.11	10.01	9.96	10.14
9.89	10.08	9.92	9.93	9.95	10.01
10.04	10.09	10.13	9.96	9.81	9.80
9.94	9.94	9.76	9.95	9.85	9.97
9.76	9.98	10.19	9.95	10.15	9.84
9.96	10.11	10.05	10.22	10.04	10.09
9.97	10.04	10.04	10.00	9.81	10.10
10.01	9.91	9.97	10.19	10.04	9.89
9.94	9.79	10.03	9.80	10.03	10.18
9.93	9.97	9.98	10.02	10.06	10.02
9.90	10.08	10.01	9.87	10.02	9.98
9.72	10.00	10.07	10.13	10.17	10.04
9.82	10.07	10.01	10.05	9.96	10.11
9.90	10.01	9.86	9.88	9.79	9.92
10.01	10.16	9.93	10.01	10.08	10.03
10.12	10.03	9.99	10.04	9.92	10.00
10.04	10.05	10.14	9.88	9.95	10.00
9.97	10.07	10.03	9.95	10.03	9.96
10.00	10.14	9.98	9.99	10.03	9.99
9.97	9.98	10.10	10.06	10.02	9.97
10.16	10.02	10.19	10.09	9.99	10.00
9.99	10.06	10.03	9.97	9.99	9.73
10.07	10.06	10.03	9.86	9.98	10.25
10.00	9.95	10.17	9.85	9.98	9.99

(a) Compile a random sample having 25 members and work out their average value.
(b) Compile a systematic sample having 25 members and work out their average value.
(c) If the population is now taken to be of a nature such that it can be divided into the following four groups:
  (i) values 1–108 (inclusive),
 (ii) values 109–144 (inclusive),
(iii) values 145–216 (inclusive), and
(iv) values 217–300 (inclusive),
compile a stratified sample having 25 members and work out their average value.
(d) Average all 300 values. Explain clearly why it is rather unlikely that *any* of the averages (a), (b) or (c) will agree exactly with the average (d).
(e) Suppose you were confronted with the above data and were told that it definitely related to a non-stratified population. If it was vital to have a reasonably good estimate of the average value *quickly*, which type of sample would you use and why?

13. A County Education Authority is concerned about the lack of employment prospects for school leavers in its area. It would like to obtain answers to the following questions:

What types of employment do school leavers wish to have?
What proportion of school leavers obtain the employment of their choice?
What proportion obtain employment outside the county?
How long does it take a school leaver to get a job?
Design a suitable questionnaire which could be given to pupils just before they leave school and returned by them six months later. Fill in suitable answers for an individual school leaver.

(J.M.B.)

14. The manager of a new restaurant wishes to cater for the requirements of the people in the locality. He would like to know how often customers are likely to dine at his restaurant and what type of food they prefer (e.g. grills, salads, snacks).
(a) Write down some of the questions which might be asked in conducting a survey to obtain the required information.
(b) State what precautions should be taken in carrying out the enquiry.
(c) Use fictitious data to represent the results of the survey in the form of tables and/or diagrams.

(W.J.E.C.)

15. (a) State briefly the chief points to be considered when preparing questions for a questionnaire.
(b) Discuss the errors which may arise in a general census of the population, and explain the circumstances under which a pilot survey would first be undertaken.

16. It is decided to obtain the views of the students of a medical college on the possibility of providing a college magazine. These are to be obtained by consulting a committee of twelve of the students. The college consists of six hundred students, 150 in the first year, 100 in each of the second, third, and fourth years, and 50 in each of the fifth, sixth, and seventh years. Describe briefly how you would select such a committee by (a) random sampling, (b) stratified sampling, and (c) quota sampling.

17. A co-educational school comprises 15 classes of 30 children and a sixth form of 150. There are equal numbers of boys and girls throughout the school. Explain how you would obtain a stratified sample of size 40.

2

Classification and tabulation of statistical data

2.1 Arrangement and classification of data

This chapter will concern itself with what we do with our statistical data, once we have collected it. Before dealing with this, however, it is important to mention a vital distinction between the two types of *quantitative variable* that will usually make up our data. Quantitative variables are those that can be given a numerical basis (as opposed to *qualitative variables* such as taste), i.e., they can be measured or counted. They can be sub-divided into *continuous variables* and *discrete variables*.

Continuous variables can take *any* value (within a certain range) and are not therefore restricted. Examples are heights, weights, and temperatures. We can have heights of 179.3 cm, 171.1 cm, etc. and we are *not* restricted to whole number (or integer) values such as 179 or 171.

Discrete variables, on the other hand, can *only* take whole number values. Examples are the daily attendances at a cinema or the number of apples in a box. Obviously, we cannot have 231.8 people attending a cinema performance or 49.42 apples in a box, and we are restricted to values such as 232 or 49. In practice, however, we can usually deal with both types of quantitative variable in much the same way.

Now, it is clearly of little help to anyone in charge of a factory, for example, to be presented with a mass of figures and to be told: 'This is the present position as far as production is concerned'. A statistician who did this would be unlikely to retain his job for long! All that the person in charge really requires is a *summary* of the figures, so arranged that they can see at a glance whether production is rising or falling, and whether action of any kind is required on their part.

Let us elaborate the above example into a real-life situation, where 'the person in charge' is an Egg Producer and the 'production figures' are the number of eggs laid per month by 500 hens.

The statistician will number the hens from 1–500. He will then arrange for the number of eggs laid daily by each hen to be carefully noted. As each day proceeds 'running totals' will be kept, until, at the end of a 28 day period, figures will be available for each of the hens. The initial data could well take the form shown in Table 2.1.

Now it is quite clear that the data in Table 2.1 is, *as it stands*, practically useless. Accordingly, we must now try and get some order out of this jumble of figures. It is a fairly obvious first step to arrange our 500 values in numerical

Table 2.1

Data   : Numbers of eggs laid by each of 500 hens
Period: 28 days

Original Data

42	25	39	35	38	25	30	18	23	43	44	21	33	34	41	45
26	53	27	33	34	9	32	11	25	45	14	21	38	28	21	34
29	42	31	24	32	18	24	11	29	22	35	20	22	33	21	41
26	21	32	38	38	42	34	42	28	19	28	36	20	30	39	27
8	28	43	11	12	23	44	31	30	29	33	25	30	24	46	27
48	52	16	26	22	19	53	25	41	23	23	24	45	33	30	21
20	22	27	31	27	12	10	48	21	32	30	22	47	37	38	34
25	24	25	26	34	40	41	29	29	33	35	17	38	41	36	33
16	39	25	27	17	14	32	22	43	27	37	31	37	32	37	24
38	39	51	26	36	25	12	17	42	29	37	24	36	39	28	34
23	24	19	28	23	31	39	53	21	7	38	13	28	25	37	21
38	27	40	21	34	33	28	51	37	27	11	36	47	27	29	14
33	25	13	29	25	34	40	34	8	43	16	18	34	36	36	17
32	18	34	35	41	36	22	40	37	15	26	28	18	30	33	50
39	27	9	34	35	34	33	37	43	33	52	34	30	21	42	15
21	23	26	18	36	34	22	35	5	28	16	20	38	39	32	23
19	33	24	35	29	34	5	31	28	22	33	28	35	45	33	39
43	38	51	29	31	25	27	40	30	20	24	12	25	44	39	15
35	28	49	26	26	35	35	44	37	17	16	16	38	24	43	37
30	21	26	28	26	26	31	30	47	39	14	26	8	10	32	24
29	31	25	29	30	30	38	37	43	47	27	32	28	22	44	19
27	13	29	23	27	21	31	33	22	20	28	14	21	19	39	23
36	50	25	46	22	31	27	22	31	40	29	42	32	44	20	29
35	35	36	33	15	46	34	29	18	27	17	39	28	28	29	31
24	24	21	28	22	32	11	24	30	40	32	38	54	31	20	32
35	27	9	12	39	6	38	23	30	26	29	13	32	32	17	39
32	26	34	18	39	30	28	29	24	31	19	14	33	24	28	31
17	16	29	49	20	37	30	31	19	38	36	50	20	36	33	20
23	25	29	31	29	29	30	37	15	23	27	45	36	27	13	23
32	24	19	37	35	36	38	24	23	20	38	50	23	26	42	36
50	52	44	31												
41	36	34	30												
27	35	22	32												
44	30	41	25												
26	33	26	37.												

order from low to high. If we do this we are in fact forming an *array*. Having done this we now have the data in the form shown in Table 2.2.

Table 2.2

Data   : Number of eggs laid by 500 hens (in ascending order)
Period : 28 days

Array of Data

5 13	17 20	22 23	25 26	27 28	30 31	32 33	35 36	38 39	42 46
5 13	17 20	22 23	25 26	27 29	30 31	32 33	35 36	38 39	42 46
6 14	17 20	22 23	25 26	27 29	30 31	32 34	35 36	38 39	42 47
7 14	18 20	22 23	25 26	27 29	30 31	32 34	35 36	38 39	43 47
8 14	18 20	22 24	25 26	27 29	30 31	32 34	35 36	38 39	43 47
8 14	18 20	22 24	25 26	28 29	30 31	32 34	35 37	38 40	43 47
8 14	18 20	22 24	25 26	28 29	30 31	32 34	35 37	38 40	43 48
9 14	18 21	22 24	25 26	28 29	30 31	33 34	35 37	38 40	43 48
9 15	18 21	22 24	25 26	28 29	30 31	33 34	35 37	38 40	43 49
9 15	18 21	22 24	25 27	28 29	30 31	33 34	35 37	38 40	43 49
10 15	18 21	22 24	25 27	28 29	30 31	33 34	35 37	38 40	43 50
10 15	19 21	22 24	25 27	28 29	30 31	33 34	35 37	38 40	44 50
11 15	19 21	22 24	25 27	28 29	30 31	33 34	35 37	38 41	44 50
11 16	19 21	23 24	25 27	28 29	30 32	33 34	36 37	38 41	44 50
11 16	19 21	23 24	25 27	28 29	30 32	33 34	36 37	39 41	44 50
11 16	19 21	23 24	25 27	28 29	30 32	33 34	36 37	39 41	44 51
11 16	19 21	23 24	26 27	28 29	30 32	33 34	36 37	39 41	44 51
12 16	19 21	23 24	26 27	28 29	30 32	33 34	36 37	39 41	44 51
12 16	19 21	23 24	26 27	28 29	30 32	33 34	36 37	39 41	44 52
12 16	19 21	23 24	26 27	28 29	31 32	33 34	36 37	39 41	45 52
12 17	20 21	23 24	26 27	28 29	31 32	33 34	36 37	39 42	45 52
12 17	20 21	23 24	26 27	28 29	31 32	33 34	36 38	39 42	45 53
13 17	20 21	23 24	26 27	28 29	31 32	33 35	36 38	39 42	45 53
13 17	20 22	23 25	26 27	28 29	31 32	33 35	36 38	39 42	45 53
13 17	20 22	23 25	26 27	28 30	31 32	33 35	36 38	39 42	46 54

Table 2.3

Frequency Distribution of Data

N.B.   We now note in brackets the number of times each value occurs:

5(2)	15(5)	25(18)	35(16)	45(5)
6(1)	16(7)	26(18)	36(17)	46(3)
7(1)	17(8)	27(21)	37(16)	47(4)
8(3)	18(8)	28(21)	38(18)	48(2)
9(3)	19(9)	29(23)	39(16)	49(2)
10(2)	20(12)	30(20)	40(7)	50(5)
11(5)	21(16)	31(19)	41(8)	51(3)
12(5)	22(15)	32(19)	42(8)	52(3)
13(5)	23(16)	33(20)	43(8)	53(3)
14(6)	24(19)	34(20)	44(8)	54(1)

We can now look at this and see whether we have manipulated the data enough. Certainly in this form our figures are more meaningful and certain facts do emerge. For example, we can see that a lot of hens lay about 30 eggs a month, whereas very few have laid more than 50 or less than 10. These facts are even easier to see if we now arrange the data into a *frequency distribution*, as shown in Table 2.3 on page 15.

The next step really follows on quite logically. Thus it ought to make the data still more meaningful (especially to a non-statistician) if we record the number of hens who lay between say 5 and 9 eggs, 10 and 14 eggs, 15 and 19 eggs, and so on. If we manipulate the data in this way we obtain what is known as a *grouped frequency distribution*:

Number of eggs	Number of hens
5–9	10
10–14	23
15–19	37
20–24	78
25–29	101
30–34	98
35–39	83
40–44	39
45–49	16
50–54	15

Now, the *Number of eggs* column comprises, in effect, a list of ten *classes*, while the *Number of hens column* likewise comprises a list of ten corresponding *frequencies*.

Two important points immediately arise. Firstly, what do we mean precisely by a *class* such as '15–19'? Secondly, what should we expect the sum of our *frequencies* column to be?

To deal with these points in order: since we are dealing with a discrete variable here, it is not particularly difficult to see that the class '15–19' will embrace the individual values 15, 16, 17, 18, and 19, but not, of course, 20. Similarly, the class '20–24' will only include 20, 21, 22, 23, and 24. Now, the reader will see, by studying the left-hand set of figures in the first column (5, 10, 15, ... , 50), that every class occupies a width of 5 (10 − 5, 15 − 10, 20 − 15, etc.), i.e. we can say that for this discrete data the class-width or class interval is 5. However, supposing that the data related instead to lengths of nails so that it was continuous, how should we now signify the various classes? The class-width can still be 5 and we can still think of the lowest permitted value for class 1 as being 5 (or more strictly 5.0). However, the greatest permitted value will now be 9.9. Similarly, for class 2 the lowest permitted value will be 10.0 while the highest will be 14.9, and so on. From this it can be seen that in the case of a continuous variable, the first class will now include all values from (and including) 5 up to (but not including) 10. The second class will include all values from (and including) 10 up to (but not including) 15, etc. Because of this we should, strictly speaking, signify these classes now as '5– ', '10– ', '15– ', ... , '50– '; however, it must be said that many statisticians still prefer to write them as '5–10', '10–15', '15–20', ... , '50–55', because they are clearer in a visual sense.

Incidentally, special care is needed when dealing with a continuous variable which has been rounded off to the nearest whole number, e.g., if weights are involved and all the values are given *to the nearest kilogram*, then classes such as '31–34', '35–38', '39–42', etc. have as their class boundaries 30.5, 34.5, 38.5, 42.5, etc., so that the class-width or class interval is in fact 4–this is not at all obvious at first sight.

Returning to the sum of our *frequencies* column, it is quite clear what the answer should be. Our original data relates to 500 hens and all we have done is rearrange this in various ways, finishing with a *classified* form. Accordingly, the frequencies column *must* also add up to 500. The reader is left to check this himself.

For many purposes, once we have classified the data, we have gone as far as we need, since a person of average intelligence could glean a considerable amount of information from it in this form.

As already mentioned, when data is tabulated in this way, it is said to be in the form of a *grouped* (or *classified*) *frequency distribution*. Often the latter will be called a *frequency distribution*, a *grouped frequency table*, and so on; however, it is probably better to use the full title in order to avoid any confusion. In a sense Grouped Frequency Distributions form the very core of elementary statistics, and several useful quantities such as the mean and the standard deviation can be calculated from them. The ways in which this can be done are described in later chapters of this book.

A query that may have formed in the reader's mind at this point is: 'Are there any *rules* with regard to the construction of a Grouped Frequency Distribution?' The answer has to be a qualified one. There are in fact no *rigid* rules, but nevertheless certain guidelines are usually followed, *viz.*:

1. *Number of classes*   We generally aim to have between 5 and 12 classes, but one cannot be too dogmatic about this.

2. *Class-width or Class-interval*   Once we have decided on the number of classes, then our *class-width* is often obvious. For example, suppose we have 200 values and have arranged these into an *array*. Suppose our lowest value is 23.7 and our highest 28.2. Let us further suppose that we have decided to have ten classes. Then an approximation to the required *class-width* will be:

$$\frac{28.2 - 23.7}{10} = 0.45$$

But 0.45 is not a particularly convenient quantity to handle, so we would almost certainly choose 0.5. Accordingly, we could have the following classes: 23.5–24.0, 24.0–24.5, 24.5–25.0, 25.0–25.5, 25.5–26.0, 26.0–26.5, 26.5–27.0, 27.0–27.5, 27.5–28.0, and 28.0–28.5; a total of ten classes in all.

It should be noted that sometimes, after we have calculated a *convenient* value for the class-width, we will need one or even two classes more than we originally intended (or perhaps one or two fewer). Generally this does not particularly matter, provided we finish up with a number between about 5 and 12.

3.   *Class-Limits*   Very often this is just a matter of common sense. For instance, in the above example we *could* have had classes: 23.45–23.95, 23.95–24.45, ..., 27.95–28.45, but from a numerical or graphical point of view such a choice would not normally be very sensible. In fact, if we do any further calculations using these data, classes of 23.5–24.0, etc., will prove easier to deal with. (See also later chapters on the mean and the standard deviation.)

2.2   Diagrammatic representation of a grouped frequency distribution — the histogram

In a sense, *histograms* could form part of Chapter 3, since they *are* diagrammatic devices for illustrating particular types of statistical data. However, since most *histograms* are derived from grouped frequency distributions and are, moreover, probably the most important type of statistical diagram, we shall deal with them here. The derivation of the word histogram is interesting — it actually comes from the Greek word *histos*—a mast; so the word histogram literally means 'mast' diagram; a loose translation, then, is bar diagram.

Let us now construct the histogram based on the grouped frequency distribution above. We proceed as follows: on a suitably sized piece of graph paper we draw a *horizontal axis* and superimpose on it a scale running from 5 to 55, marked off at 5-unit intervals. Next we draw a *vertical axis* and mark on it a scale running from 0 to 110, as shown in Figure 2.1.

We now insert on this diagram a *rectangle* representing the first class. The

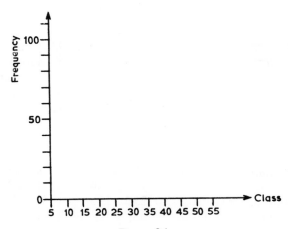

Figure 2.1

first class runs from 5–10 and has a frequency of 10, so our diagram is marked as shown in Figure 2.2.

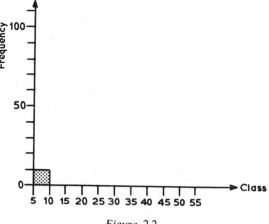

Figure 2.2

We repeat the process for the remaining nine classes, and obtain the following *histogram* (Figure 2.3).

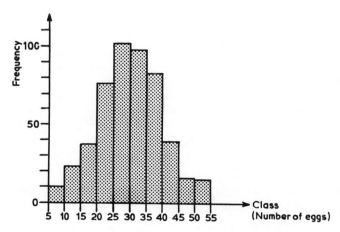

Figure 2.3 Histogram based on the eggs laid by 500 hens

In the above example, the reader can see that the plotting of each rectangle is done in the same way and there are no snags. However, it can also be seen that *all* the *class-widths* are the same, *viz.*: 5. If, in a particular grouped frequency distribution, the *class-widths* are *not* all the same, we have to proceed with considerable caution!

For reasons that will be appreciated later, there is a golden rule that must be followed for all *histograms*. This demands that the *area* of each rectangle must be directly proportional to the corresponding *frequency*. If all the rec-tangles have the same horizontal width (as they will if all the class-widths are equal), application of the above rule means that, *in practice*, we can think of the *height* of each rectangle as representing *frequency*. This is how the histogram in Figure 2.3 was plotted. Let us now consider what we have to do if we have a grouped frequency distribution with *varying* class-widths.

Consider the following data:

Class	Frequency
0– 5	5
5–15	25
15–30	85
30–45	80
45–55	20
55–65	5

We can plot the first rectangle of the corresponding histogram in the normal way (see Figure 2.4). Note that we do *not* label the vertical axis 'Frequency'.

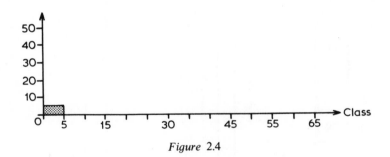

Figure 2.4

The *area A*, of each rectangle is to be directly proportional to the correspond-ing *frequency, f*. From our first rectangle:

$$5 \times 5 \text{ units of } area \equiv 5 \text{ units of } frequency$$

i.e. 1 unit of *frequency* requires 5 units of *area* (by simple proportion).

Let us now plot the second rectangle. The class '5–15' contains 25 values, and therefore our second rectangle requires $25 \times 5 = 125$ units of *area*. Our *class-width* is 10 (15 − 5), so we must give the rectangle a height, *h*, such that its area is 125 units.

$$\text{Area of rectangle} = \text{Horizontal width} \times \text{Vertical height}$$

i.e.

$$125 = 10 \times h$$

thus,
$$125 = 10h$$
$$\Rightarrow h = 12.5.$$

Therefore our second rectangle must have a height of $12\frac{1}{2}$ (as shown in Figure 2.5.).

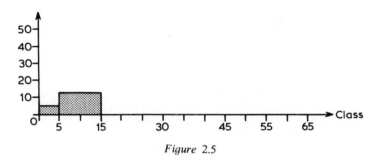

Figure 2.5

It is strongly recommended that the reader works out the heights required for the remaining rectangles and plots the entire histogram. If this is done correctly, Figure 2.6 will be obtained.

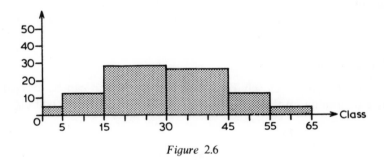

Figure 2.6

N.B.   In many situations it obviously simplifies matters if we make the area of each rectangle numerically equal to the frequency; we then have

$$\text{Class-width} \times \text{Height} = \text{Frequency}$$

so that the *height* of each rectangle is quickly obtained as:

$$\text{Height} = \frac{\text{Frequency}, f}{\text{Class-width}, c.w.}$$

Thus, to take a perfectly general case, if we have the following data we can plot it as shown in Figure 2.7.

Class (variable)	Frequency	Height ($= f/c.w.$)
10–20	20	$20 \div 10 = 2$
20–40	60	$60 \div 20 = 3$
40–65	75	3
65–85	80	4
85–95	10	1

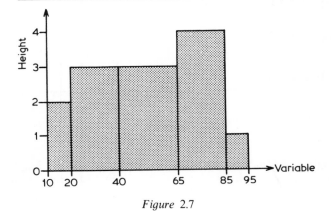

Figure 2.7

Sometimes, if we are presented with this type of histogram and given no other information, we may have to assume that the particular areas involved give the corresponding frequencies.

2.3 Frequency polygons

Frequency polygons are closely related to *histograms* and can be derived from the latter by joining up the mid-points of the tops of adjoining rectangles with

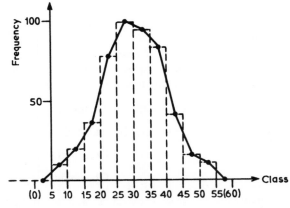

Figure 2.8 Frequency polygon based on the eggs laid by 500 hens

straight lines. If we take the histogram based on egg production (Figure 2.3), we obtain the frequency polygon shown in Figure 2.8.

Note that in order to complete the *frequency polygon*, we have to add two extra classes to the original grouped frequency distribution, *viz.* '0–5' and '55–60', giving each of these classes *zero* frequency. From Figure 2.8 it is not too difficult to see that the total area beneath the frequency polygon is the same as the sum of the areas of the rectangles of the original histogram. In other words, just as the *total* area of a histogram represents the total frequency, the total area beneath a frequency polygon also represents the total frequency.

2.4   Types of frequency distribution

The frequency polygon illustrated in Figure 2.8 approximates quite closely to the following bell-shaped curve (Figure 2.9).

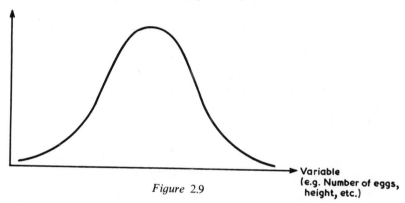

Figure 2.9

Many frequency distributions are good approximations to this symmetrically-shaped curve which is known as the *normal curve*. It should be noted that once again the total area beneath the curve represents the total frequency.

Not all frequency distributions are of the above type, however, and some of the other common types are listed below.

1.   Frequency distributions with the peak displaced to the *left* (Figure 2.10).

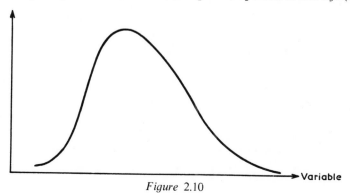

Figure 2.10

Such a distribution is no longer symmetrical and is said to exhibit *positive skew*.

2. Frequency distributions with the peak displaced to the *right* (Figure 2.11). This distribution exhibits *negative skew*.

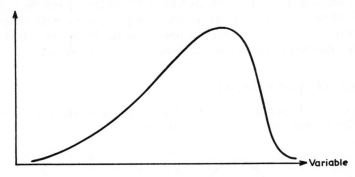

Figure 2.11

3. J-shaped frequency distributions (Figure 2.12). These distributions are so-called for obvious reasons.

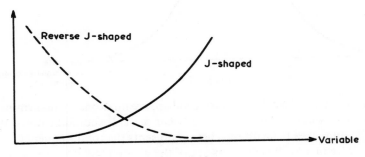

Figure 2.12

4. Bi-modal frequency distributions (Figure 2.13).

Figure 2.13

These distributions are said to be bi-modal because they contain two peaks (or modes); it should be noted that they are not necessarily asymmetrical.

5.   Rectangular frequency distributions (Figure 2.14).

If the variable concerned is discrete, all the permitted values occur with the same frequency, and the distribution is said to be *uniform*. If, however, a continuous variable is involved the distribution is known as *rectangular*.

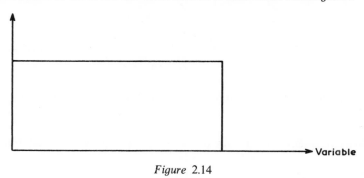

Figure 2.14

6.   Triangular frequency distributions (Figure 2.15).

The distribution of scores obtained when two ordinary dice are thrown a large number of times is of this type.

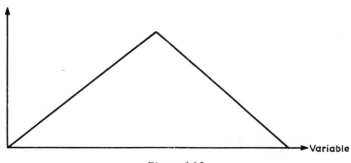

Figure 2.15

2.5   Coefficient of skewness

Sometimes we may need to have a measure of just how much a given frequency distribution is positively or negatively skewed. In a frequency distribution that is perfectly bell-shaped or 'normal' the three quantities: the mean, the median, and the mode (dealt with in detail in Chapter 5), are all equal, as shown in Figure 2.16.

N.B.   The *mean* is the arithmetic mean value, the *median* is the central value, and the *mode* is the most frequently occurring value.

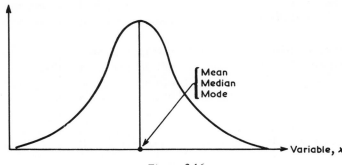

Figure 2.16

However, should the distribution exhibit positive skew, for example, the *median* and *mode* will be displaced leftwards, relative to the *mean*, as shown in Figure 2.17.

N.B. A useful memory aid – 'mean', 'median', and 'mode' are in alphabetical order.

The greater the degree of positive skew, the greater the difference between (a) the mean and the mode, and (b) the mean and the median.

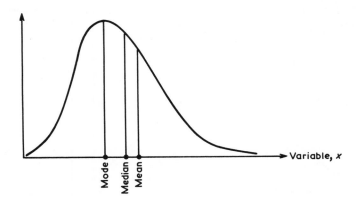

Figure 2.17

In order to give us a suitable measure of skewness, Pearson has evolved the following formula:

$$Coefficient\ of\ Skewness = \frac{Mean - Mode}{Standard\ Deviation}$$

It is not always convenient to use the mode, and since there is an empirical relationship between the mean, median, and mode, i.e.

$$Mean - Mode \simeq 3\ (Mean - Median)$$

we can, if we wish, use the alternative formula:

$$Coefficient\ of\ Skewness = \frac{3\,(\text{Mean} - \text{Median})}{\text{Standard Deviation}}$$

The mean, median, and mode are fully discussed in Chapter 5. The standard deviation (and other measures of dispersion or spread) is discussed in Chapter 6.

Exercise 2

1. 80 students took an examination, where the maximum mark possible was 100, and the following results were obtained:

Marks	Frequency
10–19	1
20–29	8
30–39	12
40–49	20
50–59	18
60–69	10
70–79	7
80–89	4

(a) What is the class-width?
(b) State which class the mark 30 would go in.
(c) Given that the class of greatest frequency is called the modal class, state which class this is.
(d) Plot a histogram to illustrate the given data.

2. The weights, to the nearest kilogram, of fifty animals of the same species are given below.

```
34   38   30   31   37   43   38   37   32   40
41   34   37   36   32   38   41   35   37   38
35   37   32   40   39   31   33   37   37   43
34   35   39   41   37   38   38   41   43   30
32   36   32   35   38   34   38   37   34   36
```

(a) Using seven equal class intervals, construct a grouped frequency table.
(b) What are the smallest and largest true values that could be included in the last interval of your table?
(c) Draw the histogram for your Grouped Frequency Distribution.
(d) What is the modal class of your Grouped Frequency Distribution?

(W.J.E.C.)

3. The distribution of incomes in a certain establishment was as follows:

Income(£)	2000–	2200–	2400–	2600–	2800–	3000–3600
Number of employees	8	16	36	40	34	26

Draw a histogram of the distribution.

(A.E.B.)

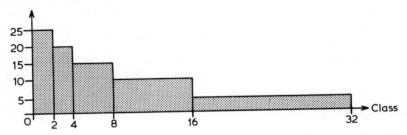

Figure 2.18

4. Complete the table below which relates to a continuous variable and pertains to the histogram shown in Figure 2.18.

Class	0–2	?	?	?	?	?
Frequency	25	?	?	?	?	?

5. Complete the table below corresponding to the histogram shown in Figure 2.19.

Class	0–?	?	3–?
Frequency	15	?	?

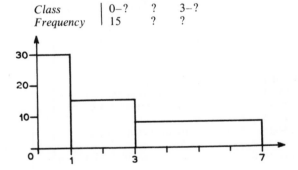

Figure 2.19

6. The masses of fruit of a certain species were determined to the nearest gram and tabulated as follows:

Mass(g)	10–12	13–15	16–18	19–21
Number of fruit	8	13	16	6

What is the class-width?

(A.E.B.)

7.

Class(£)	0–1000	1000–	1200–	1500–	2000–	3000–5000
Frequency	7	22	51	69	45	17

If, when plotting the histogram, the height of the rectangle representing the class 1000– is 22 units, what should be the height of the rectangle representing the class 2000–?

8. The marks obtained by sixty candidates in an examination were as follows:

Marks	20–29	30–39	40–49	50–59	60–69	70–79
Number of candidates	4	10	16	19	8	3

Plot a histogram based on the above data.

9. Name a feature of a magazine that is:
    (a) a discrete variable,
    (b) a continuous variable.

    (A.E.B.)

10. State whether the following variables are continuous or discrete: temperature, weight, goal, length, age, cinema attendance.

11. The variable x represents the total number of people using a municipal swimming bath in a day. Classify x as
    (a) continuous or discrete,
    (b) qualitative or quantitative.

    (A.E.B.)

12. Give an example of a qualitative variable.

13. Which of the following is a qualitative variable?
    A. Taste.
    B. Height.
    C. Cinema attendance.
    D. Temperature.

14.

Class (years)	0 and under 2	2 and under 4	4 and under 6
Frequency	60	60	60

The table relates to a continuous variable. What is the magnitude of the class-width?
A. 1.95 years.
B. 1.99 years.
C. 2 years
D. 3 years.

15. Which of the following is the basic property of a histogram?
    A. The area of a given rectangle is proportional to the frequency of the corresponding class.
    B. The rectangles must be higher in the middle than at the ends.
    C. The class-widths must all be equal.
    D. The height of each rectangle is proportional to the frequency of the corresponding class.

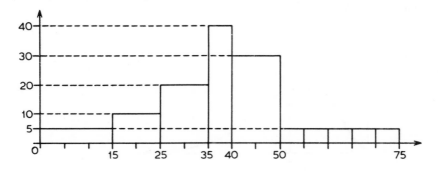

Figure 2.20

16. What is the total frequency of the distribution in Figure 2.20 on page 29?
  A. 110.
  B. 30.
  C. 1100.
  D. 1000.

17. The distribution of incomes between £250 and £3000 in the United Kingdom in 1965 is given in the following table:

Income(£)	250–500	500–1000	1000–1500	1500–2000	2000–3000
Frequency (millions)	6	9.6	5.5	1.5	0.3

Construct a histogram to show the distribution.

(L.U.)

18. Sketch frequency distributions which are (a) J-shaped, (b) bi-modal.

(A.E.B.)

19. Sketch a frequency distribution in which the mode is larger than the mean.

(A.E.B.)

20. From Figure 2.21 draw the corresponding frequency polygon.

(A.E.B.)

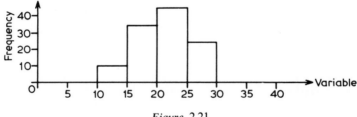

Figure 2.21

21. Sketch the outline of a positively skew histogram.

22. A variable x has a moderately skew distribution, as shown in Figure 2.22. The vertical line at A divides the area under the curve into two equal parts. State the usual name for the value A.

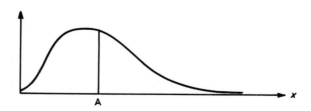

Figure 2.22

23. A frequency polygon is shown in Figure 2.23. From the diagram draw the corresponding histogram.

(A.E.B.)

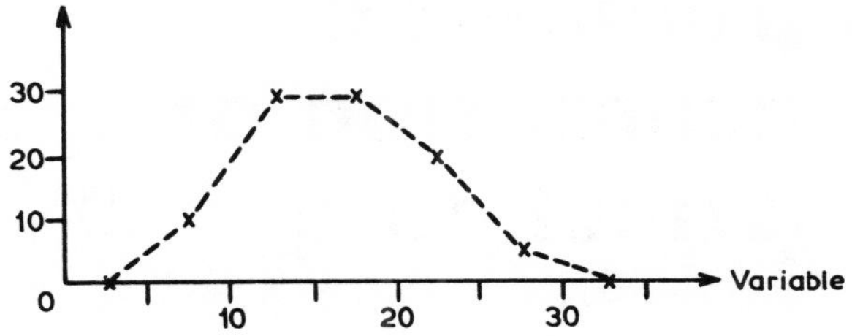

Figure 2.23

3

Diagrammatic representation of statistical data

The main purpose of the diagrammatic representation of statistical data is to make the collected data more easily understood. Other purposes are to emphasise any fluctuations which may be present, and to try and make the material as attractive to look at as possible (this is the easiest and probably the best method of persuading people to study statistical data!).

We have already described one method of diagrammatically presenting certain collected data, namely, using a histogram to represent a grouped frequency distribution. Since a histogram with all the class-widths the *same* is really just a kind of *bar chart*, we shall begin this chapter by looking at this group of diagrams.

3.1 Bar charts (or block diagrams)

If we return for a moment to the subject of histograms, the reader will recall that, provided all the class-widths are equal, the *height* of each rectangle is directly proportional to the corresponding *frequency*. This illustrates nicely the basic idea behind a *bar chart*.

A bar chart comprises a number of spaced rectangles, which generally have their major axes *vertical* (although this is by no means always the case). They can be used to represent a large variety of statistical data, including data that can be represented in other ways.

Let us consider a simple example. Suppose we have some data relating to the number of cars sold each year, over a five-year period, by Supercars Ltd:

Year	1968	1969	1970	1971	1972
Number of cars sold (to nearest 1000)	141 000	225 000	205 000	108 000	192 000

We can represent this data by the bar chart shown in Figure 3.1.

Notice that it is now easy to see the variations in *actual* car-sales for this

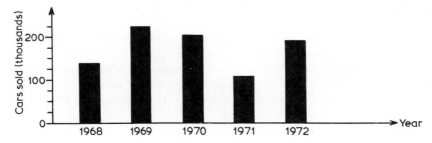

Figure 3.1 Number of cars sold by Supercars Ltd

five-year period, although, it is not so easy to estimate either the *relative* numbers of cars sold each year nor the *total* numbers sold.

3.2   Comparative bar charts

Bar charts often prove most useful if we have two (or more) sets of comparable data, and wish to compare and contrast them. For example, suppose that, apart from the data about Supercars Ltd, we also have the corresponding figures for one of Supercars' competitors, Autobig Corporation, i.e.:

Year	1968	1969	1970	1971	1972
Cars sold (*Supercars*)	141 000	225 000	205 000	108 000	192 000
Cars sold (*Autobig*)	132 000	195 000	198 000	149 000	247 000

We can represent this data by means of a *comparative bar chart*, and this time we shall have *two* bars for each year. We shall also need an explanatory key to distinguish between the two companies, as shown in Figure 3.2.

The diagram not only makes the actual numbers of cars involved clear, but also makes it easy for the eye to gauge the relative positions of each company, year by year. Of course, we might have figures for Supercars and *two* of their competitors, and in this case we would have three bars for each year, and so on.

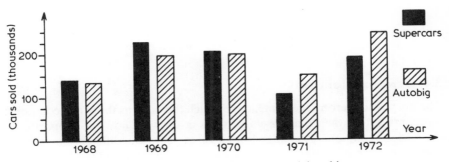

Figure 3.2 Cars sold by Supercars and Autobig

3.3   Component bar charts (or sectional bar charts)

As the name suggests, with this type of diagram each bar is now subdivided into two or more *components*. Let us imagine, once again, that we have further data from Supercars Ltd, this time concerning the personnel of the company. Suppose the personnel department supplies us with data giving a breakdown of the numbers of different kinds of employee for the years 1969–1973 inclusive, as follows:

Year	1969	1970	1971	1972	1973
Number of employees	62 000	62 000	45 000	53 000	49 000
Manual	54 400	54 400	37 800	46 000	42 700
Clerical	6 400	6 400	6 200	6 200	5 600
Executive	1 200	1 200	1 000	800	700

We can represent this data on a *component bar chart* as shown in Figure 3.3.

It is easy to discern two main features from Figure 3.3: firstly, we can see how the *total* number of employees has fluctuated from year to year and, secondly, we can get a good idea of the make-up of this total in terms of the *proportions* of staff who are manual, clerical or executive. However, it is *not* easy to decipher from this type of diagram the *actual numbers* involved.

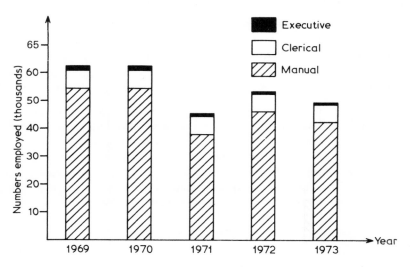

Figure 3.3 Employees of Supercars Ltd

3.4   Percentage bar charts

The purpose of percentage bar charts is much the same as those of a component bar chart in that their main usefulness lies in showing how the proportions of the various components change from year to year. The difference is that each component is now expressed as a *percentage* of the total, and the *height* of each bar remains *constant* – representing 100 per cent.

As an example, suppose a particular farmer produced the following tonnages of potatoes, sugar beet, and wheat for three consecutive years:

Crops	Year I	Year II	Year III
Potatoes	1000	1000	2000
Sugar Beet	1500	2250	750
Wheat	200	100	100
Totals	2700	3350	2850

Expressing the data as percentages of each year's total production we get the following figures:

Crops	Year I	Year II	Year III
Potatoes	37 $\left(\frac{1000}{2700} \times 100\right)$	30	70
Sugar Beet	56	67	26
Wheat	7	3	4
Totals	100	100	100

This data would then give us the *percentage bar chart* shown in Figure 3.4.

While clearly displaying the *proportions* of each crop produced, the obvious disadvantage of this type of bar chart is that it gives no details of *actual* production figures.

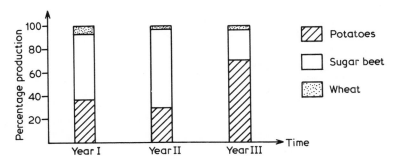

Figure 3.4 Percentage bar chart on crop production

3.5   Line charts

Statistical data will frequently be in a form where several alternative methods of diagrammatic representation can be used. For example, such a situation occurs when we have a discrete frequency distribution, where our variable, as the reader may recall, can only take whole-number values. Thus, we might have the following data:

Value, x	Frequency, f
0	4
1	7
2	15
3	5
4	2

We *could* convert this data into a pseudo-grouped frequency distribution, by choosing class limits that are *fractional*:

Class	Frequency, f
$-\frac{1}{2} - +\frac{1}{2}$	4
$\frac{1}{2} - 1\frac{1}{2}$	7
$1\frac{1}{2} - 2\frac{1}{2}$	15
$2\frac{1}{2} - 3\frac{1}{2}$	5
$3\frac{1}{2} - 4\frac{1}{2}$	2

and then plot this as a histogram, as shown in Figure 3.5.

This type of histogram can also be presented in the form of a frequency bar chart, and in this case, instead of marking off the horizontal axis with class limits, each rectangle or bar is labelled to indicate which particular discrete value it represents. Our original data gives us the bar chart shown in Figure 3.6.

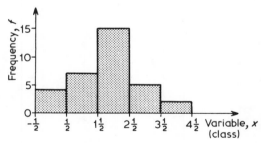

Figure 3.5

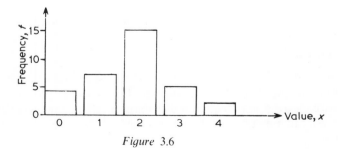

Figure 3.6

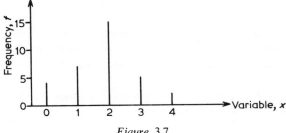

Figure 3.7

However, bearing in mind that the data *is* discrete, it is probably more realistic to represent it in the form of a *line chart*, where the *height* of each line represents the *frequency* of each value, as shown in Figure 3.7.

3.6   Pictograms

In cases where our data can be represented by a bar chart, we can often present the same data in the form of a *pictogram*.

A *pictogram* is, as its name suggests, a *picto*rial dia*gram*, and its nature can best be illustrated by referring to an example. Consider the following data which relates to the number of trees felled on a particular plantation:

Year	1968	1969	1970	1971	1972
Number of trees felled	7400	11 200	10 700	5600	9800

If we construct a pictogram, where the symbol 🌲 represents 1000 trees, we get the following result.

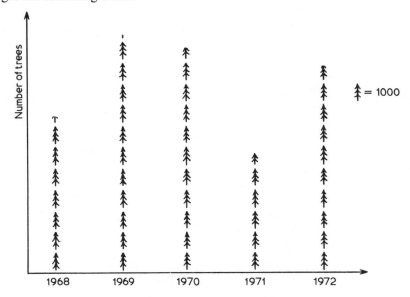

Figure 3.8 Number of trees felled

Several points should be made about pictograms:

1. In a way pictograms are merely a special kind of bar chart, where the *height* of each bar represents the *quantity* involved, and each 'bar' is split up into a series of pictorial elements which are appropriate to the particular data.

2. As with some types of bar chart, we need an explanatory key e.g. ♠ = 1000 trees, or 🏠 = 100 houses, and so on.

3. Like bar charts, pictograms usually make it easy for the eye to take in the fluctuations occurring from year to year.

4. Pictograms are an *attractive* way of representing data. They make statistics more fun, and for this reason, if for no other, they may be looked at when other methods of presenting the same data (e.g. tables of figures, bar charts or graphs) might be ignored.

5. By their very nature it is not easy to estimate the precise numbers involved, and this is an obvious disadvantage.

3.7   Comparative pictograms

These are not unlike comparative bar charts and are generally used to compare data varying from year to year where this suggests a pictorial method. To give a rather gruesome example, suppose we know the number of fatal road-accidents in Britain for the three consecutive Christmases of 1970, 1971, and 1972 (these figures are purely hypothetical):

Christmas	1970	1971	1972
Road deaths	20	25	40

An obvious symbol to use here is a coffin! Now, we could use an ordinary pictogram where ⬛ equals one death. But we can also design our pictogram in a different way using only one coffin for each year, and making the *area* of the coffin directly proportional to the number of deaths it represents.

For example, let the actual *area* of our first coffin be A units, and let it have a *height* of h units. Then

$$A \text{ units of } area \text{ equals } 20 \ deaths$$

therefore $1 \ death$ requires $\dfrac{A}{20}$ units of *area*

so for 25 deaths we require

$$25 \times \frac{A}{20} \text{ units of area} = 1.25A$$

i.e. the area of our second coffin should be 1.25 times the area of our first; the *height* of our second coffin, therefore, should be $\sqrt{1.25}$ times the height of the first. Accordingly, it should have a height of $h \times \sqrt{1.25}$ units, which is approximately 1.1h. Similarly, the reader should be able to deduce that the third coffin will have a height of about 1.4h units.

Our final pictogram, therefore, will take the form shown in Figure 3.9.

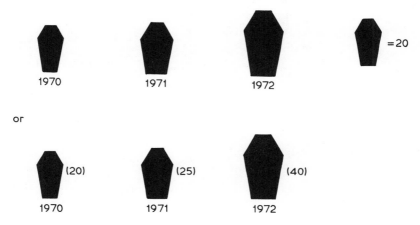

Figure 3.9 Road deaths at Christmas

3.8   Pie charts (or circular diagrams)

The word 'pie' comes from the pronunciation of the Greek alphabet letter π, leading us to suspect that circles are involved in *pie-charts*.

Pie charts are extensively used nowadays, and the reader need only look at, say, the financial pages of the *Daily Telegraph* or the *Financial Times* to see many examples. Rather than trying to give a laboured description of when a pie chart may be used, let us give an example. Suppose we possess the following information concerning central-heating installations in domestic households in the United Kingdom:

Type of central heating	Number of Households (millions)
Gas-fired	18.00
Electric	9.00
Oil-fired	11.25
Solid fuel	6.75
Total	45.00

We can now construct a pie chart to illustrate this. We start by drawing a circle of a reasonable size from the visual aspect say, for example, one having a radius of about 4 cm, as shown in Figure 3.10, which is not drawn to scale.

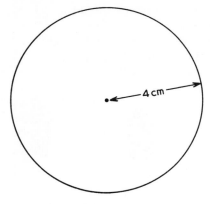

Figure 3.10

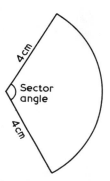

Figure 3.11 Sector of circle in Figure 3.10

Next, we divide this circle up into a number of *sectors*. A sector is rather like a slice out of a circular cake; that is to say it is an *area* bounded by two radial lines and part of the *circumference* of the circle, as shown in Figure 3.11.

Let us now consider how to calculate the *sector angle* that is going to represent gas-fired installations. There are 18 million of these, so if we let *area* be directly proportional to *quantity*, the gas-fired sector must occupy $\frac{18}{45}$ of the area of our circle. Since one complete revolution of a radial line about the centre of a circle sweeps through an angle of 360°, it can be seen that the required angle will equal:

$$\tfrac{18}{45} \times 360° = 144°$$

Using a protractor to construct this angle we obtain our gas-fired sector as shown in Figure 3.12.

If we now apply the above type of calculation to the remaining data, we finish up with the diagram shown in Figure 3.13.

Of course, we do not actually present the data like this. As with several other cases already dealt with in this chapter, we supply a key and *omit* the

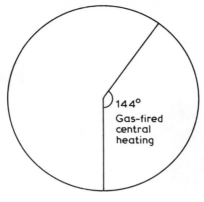

Figure 3.12

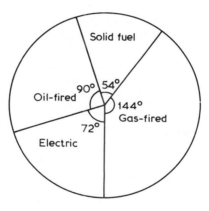

Figure 3.13

sector angles from the final diagram. Our pie chart, as finally presented, might therefore look like Figure 3.14 on the following page.

In general, therefore, in what circumstances is a pie chart appropriate? The above example suggests the answer: if we have some statistical data which relates to a particular 'whole', such as central-heating installations, annual company expenditure or foreign visitors to the U.K., etc., and we know how that 'whole' is made up, then a pie chart may be the best method. A qualification has to be added. If the total data is sub-divided into a large number of separate components, i.e. more than about seven or eight, the resulting pie chart will have too many sectors to make it visually useful. Four or five sectors are ideal, for then the eye can make a very good estimate of the relative amounts of each component present.

It should also be kept in mind that a pie chart is especially useful for dealing with data where actual numerical quantities are not so important. For example, a shareholder of a company will be far more interested in knowing what *percen-*

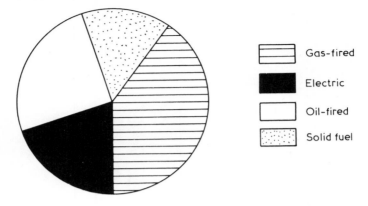

Figure 3.14 Central-heating installations in the U.K.

tage of the profits are paid out in dividends, than in knowing the absolute amount. All he wants to know, in other words, is whether he is getting a fair slice of the cake! For this very reason company results are often summarized in the form of pie charts.

Finally, one cannot be too dogmatic in statistics and there will be many cases where pie charts are just one of a number of acceptable methods for representing the same set of data.

3.9   Comparative pie charts

Let us describe these also by means of a hypothetical example. Suppose Monici Chemicals achieves the following results for the years 1972/1973 and 1973/1974:

Results	1972/1973 (£m)	1973/1974 (£m)
Total profits (after tax)	3.0	4.5
Dividends	1.3	1.4
Employee bonuses	0.4	0.5
Company reserves	1.3	2.6

Let us now construct a pie chart for 1972/1973 by the method already discussed, employing a circle of radius 2 cm, as shown in Figure 3.15.

Before constructing the pie chart for 1973/1974, we first need to know what radius it should have, and we proceed to calculate this as follows. In Figure 3.15, a circle of radius 2 cm represents total profits of £3.0m, i.e.

£3.0m is represented by a circle of area 4π square centimetres (cm^2),

so £1.0m should be represented by a circle of area $4\pi \div 3 = \frac{4}{3}\pi$ cm^2;

so £4.5m should be represented by a circle of area $\frac{4}{3}\pi \times 4.5 = 6\pi$ cm^2.

Let the radius in cm of our second pie chart be R : its area in cm^2 will then be πR^2. But we know that the area has to be 6π cm^2.

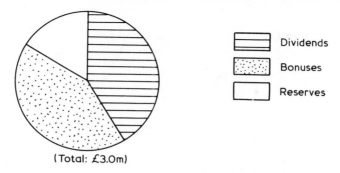

Figure 3.15 Allocation of profits: 1972/1973

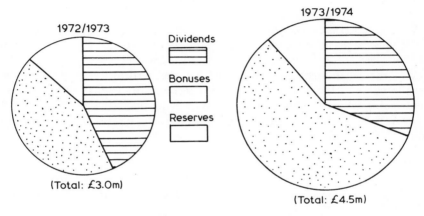

Figure 3.16 Monici Chemicals – Allocation of profits (after tax)

Hence

$$\pi R^2 = 6\pi$$

so

$$R^2 = 6$$

and

$$R \simeq 2.4\,\text{cm}$$

N.B.   We do *not* need to substitute the numerical value for π.

Thus, our second pie chart must have a radius of 2.4 cm and our complete presentation of the above data will be as shown in Figure 3.16.

3.10   Graphical presentation

Graphical presentation is one of the commonest methods used. We have all seen cartoons featuring the sales director's office in some mythical company. Whatever the point of the cartoon, almost inevitably on the wall behind his desk will be a sales chart, and it will invariably take the form shown in Figure 3.17

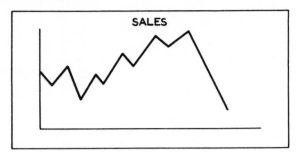

Figure 3.17

with the catastrophic drop in sales being explained in some way by the cartoon itself.

A sales chart is one example of graphical presentation of statistical data, and it may be useful if we look at it in slightly more detail. Firstly, we should ask ourselves what the *horizontal* and *vertical* axes represent.

A moment's thought should tell us that the vertical axis represents *sales* (i.e. the value of the goods sold by the company or perhaps the quantity of goods sold), whilst the horizontal axis represents *time*.

Let us now illustrate all this by looking at the sales figures of some imaginary firm:

Sales figures of Wunderwash Washing-Machines Ltd for 1969–1973

Year	1969	1970	1971	1972	1973
Sales (£)	420 000	370 000	360 000	380 000	540 000

This original data can be represented graphically as shown in Figure 3.18.

It should be mentioned here that unfortunately there are ways in which the above type of data can be distorted, and consequently mislead the unwary

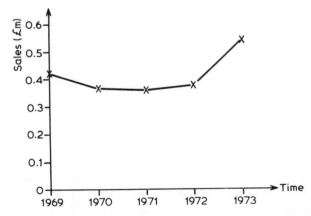

Figure 3.18 Wunderwash Washing-Machines Ltd – Sales : 1969/1973

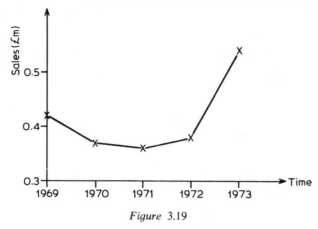

Figure 3.19

reader. For example, an unscrupulous sales director who joined Wunderwash in May 1971 and wanted to impress the other directors with the fact that the performance of the company had been nothing short of spectacular since his joining, could present the above data as shown in Figure 3.19.

Can the reader spot what is dishonest about this type of graph?

Assuming, however, that the above type of distortion is not present, graphs can and do provide an extremely useful method of presenting statistical data in a form, moreover, that the majority of people are able to understand.

Finally, it should be noted that graphs of the type just discussed form part of a family known as *time series*. Time series can be used to illustrate any data where the variable concerned changes (or can change) with time. Since time series are dealt with in detail in Chapter 8, it is not proposed to discuss them further here.

3.11 Tabular presentation

All the different types of diagrammatic and pictorial presentation of data previously dealt with in this chapter are originally based on a *table* of some kind. These tables form an important method of presentation in their own right, since for some kinds of statistical data, a well-conceived table is very often sufficient, and makes more elaborate diagrams unnecessary. For example, suppose we are provided with the following information relating to the coal output of two different coal-mines for the years 1976, 1977, and 1978:

‘Mine A has consistently achieved the higher production-rate (currently 2 500 000 tonnes per year), and even in the very difficult year of 1976 still exceeded the output of Mine B by some 500 000 tonnes. In contrast the problems besetting Mine B have still not been resolved, and in some respects have grown worse. Thus its current production (1 400 000 tonnes) is no improvement on 1977 and is indeed some 200 000 tonnes lower than in 1976. The only year in which production at Mine B was comparable to that at Mine A was in 1977, and even here the differential was still about 400 000 tonnes.'

All the useful information contained in the above extract can be summarized in the following table:

Mine	Production figures (millions of tonnes)		
	1976	1977	1978
A	2.1	1.8	2.5
B	1.6	1.4	1.4

Accordingly, when pondering the problem of just what type of statistical presentation to use for a particular set of data, never forget the humble table! It may well be perfectly adequate.

Exercise 3

1. Briefly outline the main principles to be observed when tabulating statistical data. Design a table which will show the numbers of men and women Members of Parliament immediately after the General Elections of June 1970, March 1974, and October 1974.

2. The quantities A and B may be represented either by two lines or by two squares. If the lengths of the lines were in the ratio 2 : 1, what should the ratio of the sides of the squares be?

3. Which features does a sectional bar chart emphasize?

4. (a) Explain briefly the purposes of pictorial representation.
   (b) The employees of a large service company are classified as follows:

Senior management	Middle management	Junior management and clerical
124	693	3172

   Represent these data pictorially in two ways, using a different method of representation for each. Compare the advantages and disadvantages of the two methods used.

5. Pie charts are to be drawn to illustrate and compare the finances of a company in 1960 and 1970. What will be the radius of the 1970 chart if the radius of the 1960 chart is 10 cm?

Area of the world	Profit (£ million)	
	1960	1970
United Kingdom	20	36
Western Europe	22	28
United States	33	44

6. If a circle of radius 1 unit represents a quantity of 2000, what should be the radius of a circle which represents a quantity of 500?

7. Give two advantages of pictorial representation.

8. A farmer's yield of cereals per hectare in 1977 was:

Cereal yield (tonnes)	Wheat	Barley	Oats	Maize	Rye
	2	1	3	0.5	3.5

If the information is represented in a circular diagram, what is the angle of the sector representing maize?
A. 72°.
B. 36°.
C. 18°.
D. 54°.

9. The table below shows the quantity, in hundreds of litres, of wheat, barley and oats produced on a certain farm during the years 1971 to 1974.

Crop	1971	Quantity (litres) 1972	1973	1974
Wheat	34	43	43	45
Barley	18	14	16	13
Oats	27	24	27	34

(a) Construct a sectional bar chart to illustrate these data.
(b) For each year express the figure for each crop as a percentage of the annual total and hence construct a percentage bar chart.
(c) Comment briefly on the advantages and disadvantages of these methods of illustrating the data.

(A.E.B.)

10. In a diagrammatic representation one tonne is represented by a cube of side 1. What is the length of the side of a cube representing 8 tonnes?
A. 2.
B. $\sqrt{8}$.
C. 4.
D. 8.

11. The exports of country A are represented diagrammatically by a cube whose edge is 4 times as long as the edge of the cube representing the exports of country B. What is the ratio of A's exports to B's exports?

12. Briefly compare the advantages and disadvantages of a bar chart and a pie chart in displaying statistical data.

13. Give an example of the type of data which may be best illustrated by a sectional bar chart as shown in Figure 3.20 (page 48).

(A.E.B.)

14. (a) State briefly what diagrams you would use to illustrate the following data.
    (i) The number of marriages in your town for each month of 1977.
    (ii) The proportion of the harvest yields for 1975 of the cereal crops, wheat, barley, oats, and rye.
    (iii) The numbers of pairs of shoes of different sizes bought by the pupils of your school in 1978.

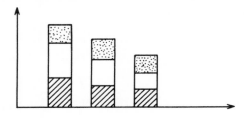

Figure 3.20

(b) The following table gives the percentage composition of meadow hay harvested at different dates.

Date of cutting	Grade protein	Fat	Soluble carbohydrates	Fibre	Ash
May 14	17.7	3.2	40.8	23.0	15.2
June 9	11.2	2.7	43.2	34.9	8.0
June 26	8.5	2.7	43.3	38.2	7.3

Illustrate the above data in one diagram.

(A.E.B.)

15. At January 1st, 1962 a firm employed 90 staff of whom 79 were men. During the year 17 staff left and 13 of these were men. The total recruitment during the year was 13 of whom 3 were women.

During 1963 wastage declined by 3 amongst men compared with 1962 and no women left. 6 more men but 2 fewer women were recruited than in the previous year.

The total number employed at 1 January 1964 amounted to 93.

Arrange the above information in concise tabular form showing all relevant totals and sub-totals.

(A.E.B.)

16. (a) State what kind of data are best illustrated by the following diagrams: (i) pie chart, (ii) bar chart, (iii) histogram.

(b) The amount of vegetables imported into the United Kingdom in the years 1953, 1957, and 1961 is given in the following table.

Vegetables	Thousand tonnes imported in		
	1953	1957	1961
Potatoes	121	254	261
Onions	199	220	222
Tomatoes	185	204	158
Others	55	67	88
Total	560	745	729

Use the above table: (i) to represent the proportions of vegetables imported in 1961 in a pie chart of radius 2 units, (ii) to calculate the radii of the circles which would effect a true comparison with the circle already drawn for the fresh vegetables imported in 1953 and 1957 if the areas of the circles are to be proportionate to the total amount of fresh vegetables imported in a year.

(A.E.B.)

17. Make up appropriate data and draw
    (a) a diagram to compare the total numbers of cars produced in each of *three* different countries in 1972,
    (b) diagrams to compare, for the same three countries, the proportions of their total productions which were exported,
    (c) graphs to illustrate and compare the numbers of cars exported annually by *two* of the countries during the period 1968 to 1972.

    (J.M.B.)

18. The table below gives the productions of two basic industries for the European Economic Community (E.E.C.) and the United Kingdom (U.K.) for the years 1960 and 1970.

	Coal (million tons)		Crude steel (million tons)	
	1960	1970	1960	1970
E.E.C.	19.5	13.7	6	9
U.K.	17	12.4	2	2.3

   Calculate the percentage changes in production between 1960 and 1970. Draw suitable diagrams to compare these percentage changes for the E.E.C. and the U.K.
   Illustrate by means of pictograms the production of coal and crude steel by the U.K. for the two given years.

    (J.M.B.)

19. Construct a table to be used to show information concerning road accidents to school children in a certain town, based upon the following details:
    classification (slight, moderate, severe); time of day; distance from nearest zebra crossing; and type of vehicle involved.
    Your table should make provision for daily totals. Fill in typical results for a particular day when four accidents were reported.

    (J.M.B.)

20. The cost of a packet of cornflakes is distributed in the following way:

Manufacture	48 per cent
Advertising	9 per cent
Freight and storage	9 per cent
Manufacturer's profit	12 per cent
Retail gross profit	22 per cent

Represent this information in a block diagram.

    (J.M.B.)

21. The following figures refer to goods transported in the United Kingdom (measured in thousands of million tonne km).

Method of transportation	Goods transported	
	1961	1971
Road	32.3	52.0
Rail	17.6	15.0
Coastal shipping	13.5	13.0

Draw a diagram to illustrate and to compare the percentage changes from 1961 to 1971 for each type of transport. Exhibit the data for 1971 in a circular diagram of radius 5 cm.

(J.M.B.)

22. The table below refers to the numbers (in thousands) of tractors and horses in use on farms in Great Britain.

	Numbers (thousands)				
	1930	1940	1950	1960	1970
Tractors	17	100	332	474	495
Farm horses	803	620	347	55	10

Draw time-series graphs to illustrate and compare these figures. Comment briefly on the trends indicated by your graphs. Draw a pictogram to illustrate the decline in the use of farm horses since 1950.

(J.M.B.)

23. The following table shows the numbers of police officers according to rank in Wales and in England.

Country	Numbers of police officers:		
	Inspectors or above	Sergeants	Constables
Wales	480	890	3 630
England	6 800	12 000	61 200

Express the numbers of police officers in each category as a percentage of the total number in that country. Draw two block diagrams, one for each country, scaled so as to be suitable for comparing the percentages according to rank in the two countries.

(W.J.E.C.)

4
Cumulative frequency distributions

4.1 Cumulative frequency distributions and their uses

Let us consider the following hypothetical grouped frequency distribution:

Class	Frequency
100–110	6
110–120	17
120–130	48
130–140	96
140–150	150
150–160	100
160–170	57
170–180	21
180–190	5
Total	500

Now, this table tells us that there are, for instance, 17 values lying between 110 and 120. It also tells us that there are $17 + 6 = 23$ values lying between 100 and 120. Similarly, $6 + 17 + 48 = 71$ values lie between 100 and 130, and so on.

Let us accept for the moment that it is sometimes useful to have this type of information; we can now construct, what is commonly called a *cumulative frequency distribution*, from the above table, which gives the results shown on the following page.

The reader can probably see that we have a very good check when we compile a cumulative frequency table, namely, that the cumulative frequency figure opposite the *highest* class must be the same as the *total* frequency. This is

Class	Cumulative frequency
100–110	6
110–120	23
120–130	71
130–140	167
140–150	317
150–160	417
160–170	474
170–180	495
180–190	500

because all the values must lie somewhere between the lower boundary of the lowest class and the upper boundary of the highest class. Thus the figure of 500 obtained here suggests that we have not made any errors.

Having completed our table, the question arises as to what we can do with it. For the moment let us make one further assumption: that a graph based on this table can also prove useful. We will explain why after we have plotted it. These *cumulative frequency graphs* or *curves* are also called *ogives*. The word *ogive*, which literally means 'diagonal vault rib' or 'pointed arch', was first used by Galton to describe S-shaped cumulative frequency curves in the late nineteenth century. Strictly speaking, therefore, its use should be confined to the latter, however, it is a conveniently *short* word to describe *any* cumulative frequency curve. The above table gives us the curve shown in Figure 4.1.

The reader will see, if he refers to the data on which it is based, that each cumulative frequency figure has been plotted against the *upper* boundary of the corresponding class. In addition, one extra point is obtained by plotting 0 against the lower boundary of the lowest class, since all the values must lie above this. Let us now see what information we can get from our graph. Supposing we wish to know the percentage of values greater than 160. We proceed as follows: find 160 on the horizontal axis and draw a vertical line from this point to the curve; from where it meets the curve draw a second horizontal line back to the vertical axis; read off the appropriate value, in this case about 415 (see Figure 4.1).

We now know that 415 values lie *below* 160 and therefore $500 - 415 = 85$ values must lie above 160. The percentage of values above 160 is given by:

$$\text{Percentage} = \tfrac{85}{500} \times 100$$
$$= 17$$

17 per cent of the values lie above 160.

In the same way we can calculate the percentage of values lying between say 130 and 150, or the percentage of values lying below 180, and so on.

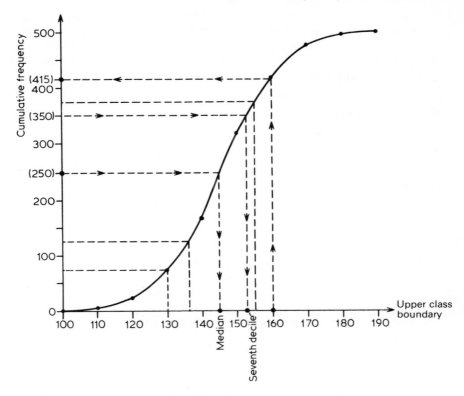

Figure 4.1 Cumulative frequency curve or ogive

The median   The use of the median value is dealt with in Chapter 5 and all we need to know for the moment is that it is the central value of a distribution, or that value such that an equal number of the remaining values lie below and an equal number above. For 500 values the median is strictly the $250\frac{1}{2}$ th value, but for all practical purposes the 250th will suffice. The reader should now try and estimate the median value from the above graph (Figure 4.1). (For the answer see below.)

The quartiles   These are also important quantities since they can be used to give us a measure of the dispersion of a distribution (see Chapter 6). There are two quartiles: the lower and the upper (strictly speaking the median is also a quartile but this need not concern us here).

The *lower quartile* (often given the symbol Q_1) is defined as that value such that a quarter of the remainder lie below, while three quarters lie above.

The *upper quartile* (often given the symbol Q_3) is the exact opposite of the lower quartile, i.e. that value such that three quarters of the remainder lie below while only a quarter lie above.

Again, the reader should try and estimate the values of both quartiles from Figure 4.1.

Deciles   The median divides our cumulative frequency graph into two parts, the two quartiles together with the median divide it into four, and as we might expect the *deciles* divide it into *ten* parts. Thus, suppose we require the value of the seventh decile: we must proceed $\frac{7}{10}$ ths of the way along our 500 values, i.e. we require the $(500 \times \frac{7}{10})$th value, or the 350th value.
From the graph the 350th value is about 152.

The seventh decile is 152.

Percentiles   These divide our graph into *one hundred* parts. Again, as an exercise the reader should see if he can estimate the value of the fifteenth percentile.

> *ANSWERS*:
>
> Median $\simeq 144$
> Lower quartile, $Q_1 \simeq 137$
> Upper quartile, $Q_3 \simeq 156$
> Fifteenth percentile $\simeq 130$

The semi-interquartile range (S.I.R.)   This is defined as:

$$\frac{\text{Upper quartile} - \text{Lower quartile}}{2}$$

or,

$$\text{S.I.R.} = \frac{Q_3 - Q_1}{2}.$$

For our particular distribution, therefore, the semi-interquartile range will be:

$$\frac{156 - 137}{2} = 9.5$$

The S.I.R. is 9.5.

The purpose of evaluating this quantity is dealt with in Chapter 6.

The calculation of medians, quartiles, etc.
Although this method is usually more convenient and easier, it is not necessary to draw a cumulative frequency graph in order to ascertain the above quantities. They can be calculated directly from the cumulative frequency distribution itself (on which the graph is based). For our purposes it will suffice if we demonstrate the calculation of the median value. The quartiles, deciles, and percentiles are all obtained in an analogous manner.
We have the following table of values:

Class	Frequency	Cumulative frequency
100–110	6	6
110–120	17	23
120–130	48	71
130–140	96	167
140–150	150	317
150–160	100	417
160–170	57	474
170–180	21	495
180–190	5	500

We require the median value, i.e. the 250th value. From the table the 167th value is 140 while the 317th value is 150. Therefore the 250th value lies somewhere in the class 140–150. Further, there are 150 values in this particular class which we assume are spread evenly across the class-width of 10.

Now the 167th value takes us up to 140, and we need to go as far as the 250th value, therefore we need to proceed a further $(250 - 167) = 83$ values, i.e. we need to go along to the 83rd out of the 150 values in this class. The portion of the class-width we will have traversed will therefore equal

$$10 \times \tfrac{83}{150} \simeq 5.5$$

therefore the actual median value will be $140 + 5.5 = 145.5$ or 146 to three significant figures.

By calculation the median value is $\simeq 146$.

The reader will see that this compares well with the value we obtained from the graph, namely 144.

At this stage it is perhaps relevant to say a little about the utility of quantities such as the median, the quartiles, and so on.

Whenever a statistician collects together a series of values for some variable or other (e.g. heights, weights, examination marks), it is always useful to know firstly, what the 'average' value is and secondly, what the 'spread' of the values is.

Any measure that helps us to estimate the 'average' value is called a 'measure of central tendency' or a 'measure of location', and amongst these measures is the median.

Likewise, any measure that helps us to estimate the 'spread' of the values is called a 'measure of dispersion', and amongst these measures is the semi-inter-quartile range.

It may help the reader to get a better understanding of measures like 'average' and 'dispersion' if we illustrate them graphically. Let us suppose that we have measured a large number of values of two variables A and B and that both come from so-called 'normal' populations. Let us consider two possibilities:

1.   Population A and Population B both have the *same* 'average' but A has a low dispersion whereas B has a high dispersion. Their frequency distributions would look as shown in Figure 4.2.

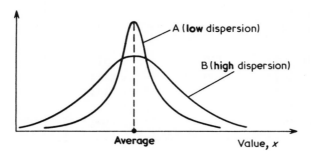

Figure 4.2

2.   Population A and Population B both have the same dispersion, but A's average is lower than B's average. This time their frequency distributions would look as shown in Figure 4.3.

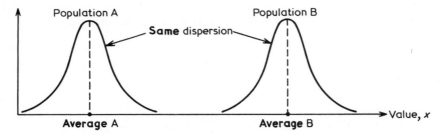

Figure 4.3

4.2   Cumulative frequency polygons

These are very similar to cumulative frequency graphs except that once all the points on the graph have been plotted, they are then joined up with straight lines as opposed to drawing a smooth curve through them. Let us return once more to the cumulative frequency distribution we have been using throughout this chapter:

Class	Cumulative frequency
100–110	6
110–120	23
120–130	71
130–140	167

Class	Cumulative frequency
140–150	317
150–160	417
160–170	474
170–180	495
180–190	500

Then this table gives us the following *cumulative frequency polygon* (Figure 4.4).

A cumulative frequency polygon can be used to estimate the median value, the lower and upper quartiles, etc., but it is liable to give less accurate results than a cumulative frequency curve or ogive – the reader should try and think why.

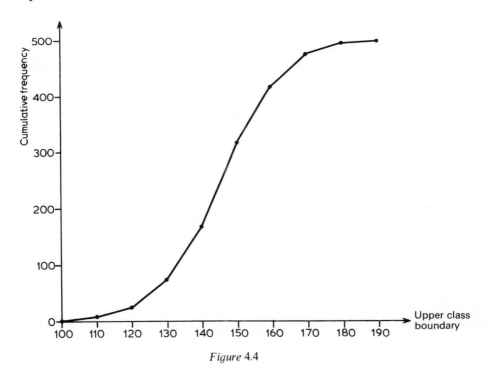

Figure 4.4

4.3   Cumulative relative frequency graphs

Sometimes it may be more convenient to plot the data of a cumulative frequency distribution in the form of a *cumulative relative frequency curve* or *polygon*. For the sake of brevity we will confine our remarks to the former (although everything discussed below can also be applied to the polygons).

To plot a cumulative relative frequency curve we proceed as follows: take the original cumulative frequency distribution data and add a further column giving each cumulative frequency as a fraction or percentage of the *total* frequency. From the distribution we have been using we then get the following result:

Class	Cumulative frequency	Cumulative relative frequency (per cent)	
100–110	6	$\frac{6}{500} \times 100 =$	1.2
110–120	23	$\frac{23}{500} \times 100 =$	4.6
120–130	71		14.2
130–140	167		33.4
140–150	317		63.4
150–160	417		83.4
160–170	474		94.8
170–180	495		99.0
180–190	500		100.0

We now plot each cumulative relative frequency value against the *upper* boundary of each class as usual (Figure 4.5).

The shape of the curve is of course unaltered but the usefulness of plotting it in this form is that we can *quickly* obtain values for the median and quartiles, etc. For example, if we require the median we read off the class value corresponding to 50 per cent; for the upper quartile we read off the value corresponding to

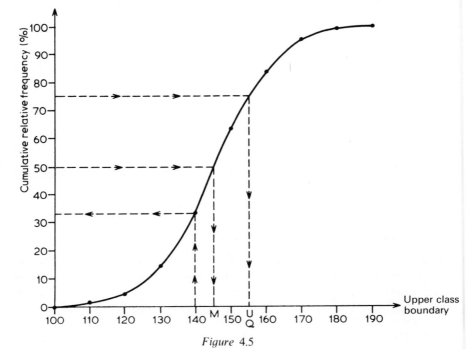

Figure 4.5

75 per cent; and so on. Also, if we require the percentage of values, say, less than 140 we read off the percentage value corresponding to this class value. All this has been illustrated on the graph in Figure 4.5 and the approximate values are listed below:

$$\text{Median} \simeq 145$$
$$\text{Upper quartile} \simeq 155$$
$$\text{Percentage of values} < 140 \simeq 32$$

N.B.   The first two values do not agree exactly with those previously obtained (144 and 156 respectively), but we should not expect this when using a graphical method.

4.4   Cumulative frequency graphs based on discrete frequency distributions

Discrete frequency distributions have already been mentioned in Chapter 3 and are dealt with again in later chapters, but it is worth mentioning here that by converting them into pseudo-grouped frequency distributions it is possible to plot cumulative frequency curves or polygons based on them.

Thus, if we consider the following discrete distribution:

Discrete variable, x	Frequency, f
3	2
4	6
5	11
6	8
7	3

we can, somewhat artificially, convert it into a grouped frequency distribution by taking classes of $2\frac{1}{2}-3\frac{1}{2}$, $3\frac{1}{2}-4\frac{1}{2}$, etc., so that we get:

Class	Frequency	Cumulative frequency
$2\frac{1}{2}-3\frac{1}{2}$	2	2
$3\frac{1}{2}-4\frac{1}{2}$	6	8
$4\frac{1}{2}-5\frac{1}{2}$	11	19
$5\frac{1}{2}-6\frac{1}{2}$	8	27
$6\frac{1}{2}-7\frac{1}{2}$	3	30

This data yields the cumulative frequency polygon shown in Figure 4.6.

From the polygon, by way of example, the following *approximate* values are obtained:

$$\text{Median} : 5.1$$
$$\text{Lower quartile} : 4.2$$

Upper quartile : 5.9
70th percentile : 5.7

(It should be noted that the true values are 5, 4, 6, and 6 respectively.)

If a cumulative relative frequency graph is required then this can be constructed as previously described.

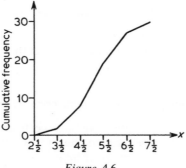

Figure 4.6

4.5 Reverse cumulative frequency distributions

Occasionally, we may come across a cumulative frequency distribution which is 'the wrong way round', e.g. consider the following table based on the weekly wages of 60 workers:

Wage(£)	Cumulative frequency
40–45	60
45–50	55
50–55	43
55–60	15
60–65	4

Such a table tells us that all 60 workers received a wage greater than £40, 55 received a wage greater than £45, and so on. We can also see that nobody received more than £65.

To plot the cumulative frequency graph in this case each cumulative frequency is plotted against the *lower* boundary of the corresponding class, and for the above data we obtain the ogive shown in Figure 4.7.

From the figure we can see, for example, that approximately 31 workers earned more than £52 per week.

In practice, when given data in the above way the safest approach, in order to avoid mistakes, is probably to convert it back to the more common form of cumulative frequency distribution *before* plotting any graphs or performing any calculations. Thus the data above readily converts as follows:

Wage(£) (1)	Cumulative frequency (2)	Frequency (3)	Ordinary cumulative frequency (4)
40–45	60	5(60–55)	5
45–50	55	12(55–43)	17
50–55	43	28	45
55–60	15	11	56
60–65	4	4	60

So, if we are asked to calculate the number of workers earning more than £49 say, using columns (1),(3), and (4) the answer will be:

$$60 - (5 + \tfrac{4}{5} \times 12) \simeq 45$$

N.B. We would obtain the same answer using columns (1),(2), and (3), for now the required number will be:

$$55 - \tfrac{4}{5} \times 12, \text{ which again gives} \simeq 45.$$

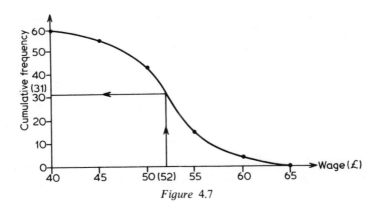

Figure 4.7

4.6 Types of cumulative frequency curve

The Grouped Frequency Distribution we considered at the beginning of this

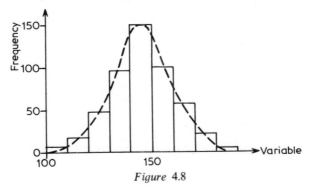

Figure 4.8

chapter gives rise to the histogram shown in Figure 4.8, and it is clear (see superimposed broken line) that this data has an approximately 'normal' distribution. Now, we already know the shape of the cumulative frequency curve based on this data, so diagrammatically we can summarize our results as follows (Figure 4.9):

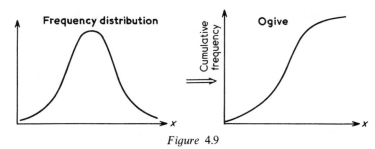

Figure 4.9

Consider now the case where the frequencies of all the classes are *equal*, e.g.

Class	Frequency	Cumulative frequency
0–5	4	4
5–10	4	8
10–15	4	12
15–20	4	16
20–25	4	20

The histogram for this data is shown in Figure 4.10, while the cumulative frequency curve is in fact a straight line (Figure 4.11):

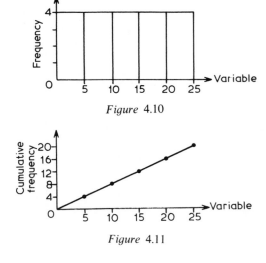

Figure 4.10

Figure 4.11

So, diagrammatically (Figure 4.12):

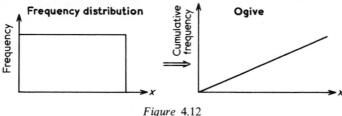

Figure 4.12

By considering various hypothetical grouped frequency distributions in the above manner, it is not too difficult to decide what type of ogive a particular distribution will have.

Problem: Sketch the ogive that is obtained from a J-shaped frequency distribution. (For the answer see the end of Exercise 4, page 70).

Exercise 4

1. Which one of the following could be a cumulative frequency curve?

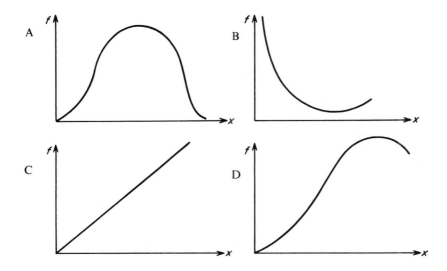

2. The table shows the intelligence quotient (I.Q.) of 90 pupils at a school.

I.Q.	65–	75–	85–	95–	105–	115–	125–	135–
Number of pupils	1	7	17	28	22	12	2	1

Each I.Q. is given correct to one decimal place. Write down the lowest and highest values that would be placed in the class 95–. Compile a cumulative frequency table from the above data and draw a corresponding cumulative frequency curve. (Take 1 cm to represent 5 units on each scale.)
From the graph estimate
(a) the median value of the I.Q.,

(b) the semi-interquartile range of the distribution,
(c) the percentage of children above average intelligence if an I.Q. of 100 is taken as average.

(A.E.B.)

3. The table below relates to wages. Estimate the percentage of workers earning between £14 and £22 per week.

Weekly wage(£)	12–	16–	20–	25–	30–50
Number of workers	22	49	45	26	8

4. The table below gives the lifetimes of 430 valves.

Lifetime (to the nearest hour)	Number of valves
300– 399	20
400– 499	49
500– 599	61
600– 699	83
700– 799	70
800– 899	64
900– 999	51
1000–1099	23
1100–1199	7
1200–1299	2
Total	430

Construct a cumulative frequency distribution table from the above data, and from it plot the corresponding cumulative frequency graph. From your graph estimate
(a) the median value of the distribution,
(b) the semi-interquartile range of the distribution,
(c) the percentage of valves expected to burn out in 550 hours,
(d) the percentage of the valves sold that the manufacturer will have to replace if he guarantees a valve to last 425 hours?

(A.E.B.)

5. The following table shows the weights, in kilograms, of 250 boys. Each weight was recorded to the nearest 100 grams.

Weight(kg)	Number of boys
44.0–47.9	3
48.0–51.9	17
52.0–55.9	50
56.0–57.9	45
58.0–59.9	46
60.0–63.9	57
64.0–67.9	23
68.0–71.9	9

Draw the ogive and use it to estimate
(a) the semi-interquartile range,
(b) the second decile,
(c) the eighty-fourth percentile,
(d) the percentage of boys weighing over 59 kilograms.

(A.E.B.)

6. The distribution of incomes in a certain establishment was as follows:

Income(£)	2000–	2200–	2400–	2600–	2800–	3000–3600
Number of employees	8	16	36	40	34	26

(a) Calculate the mean income.
(b) Draw a histogram of the distribution.
(c) Using 1 cm to represent £100 and to represent 10 employees, plot an ogive (cumulative frequency curve) of the distribution and hence find (i) the median income, (ii) the lower quartile, (iii) the upper quartile, (iv) the semi-interquartile range.

(A.E.B.)

7. Draw a cumulative frequency polygon for the data given below and determine the median from it. Also, *calculate* the median from this data.

Class	Frequency
0– 10	2
10– 20	12
20– 30	23
30– 40	36
40– 50	48
50– 60	31
60– 70	19
70– 80	7
80– 90	2
90–100	1

8. The deposit balance of 170 depositors in a rural bank is shown in the table below.

Deposit balance	Number of depositors
Less than £25	56
£25 and less than £50	33
£50 and less than £100	28
£100 and less than £150	17
£150 and less than £200	12
£200 and less than £250	11
£250 and less than £500	8
£500 and less than £1000	5

Calculate
(a) the cumulative frequencies,
(b) the median of the distribution,
(c) the semi-interquartile range of the distribution,
(d) the proportion of depositors with a balance in excess of £400.

(A.E.B.)

9. The following figures are the numbers of components of a particular type issued per day from the store-room of a factory for a period of 40 days:

53	50	61	51	58	52	57	67	53	69
45	55	42	62	54	60	57	48	63	68
56	50	63	56	58	53	52	71	59	52
55	65	50	59	54	62	46	51	73	64

Display the data in the form of a grouped frequency table using the intervals 40–44, 45–49, etc. Use this table to draw a cumulative frequency polygon for the distribution and from your graph estimate the semi-interquartile range of the distribution.

(J.M.B.)

10. In order to test the accuracy of speedometers, a number of cars are chosen at random and the speedometer readings are observed when the true speed is exactly 60 kilometres per hour (measured by a very accurate electronic device).

The table below shows the percentages of the observed readings which occur in the given intervals:

| Observed readings (km/h) | | Percentage |
exceeding	not exceeding	
50	55	18
55	60	22
60	65	43
65	70	17

Draw on graph paper a cumulative relative frequency polygon for the data. Use your graph to estimate
(a) the median of the speedometer readings,
(b) the proportion of speedometers which give readings within the legal requirements of $\pm$ 10 per cent of the true speed.

(J.M.B.)

11. A group of 20 children was asked to state how many hours (to the nearest hour) each of them spent watching television during a particular weekend. The results were:

| 3 | 6 | 5 | 3 | 3 | 4 | 5 | 5 | 0 | 4 |
| 3 | 2 | 5 | 7 | 0 | 2 | 2 | 3 | 2 | 1 |

(a) Use the data given to construct a grouped frequency table with four equal intervals. Use the table to obtain a measure of average, stating the name of the measure you obtain.
(b) Construct a cumulative frequency polygon from the values in your grouped frequency table. Use the polygon to estimate a measure of dispersion, stating the name of the measure you obtain.

(J.M.B.)

12. A large store sends out accounts to 80 customers. The table below gives the distribution of the number of days taken to settle the accounts.

| Number of days | | Number of accounts settled |
exceeding	not exceeding	
4	8	4
8	12	13
12	16	15
16	20	18
20	24	14
24	28	10
28	32	6

Draw a cumulative frequency polygon for the data. Use your graph to estimate
(a) the semi-interquartile range of the distribution,
(b) the percentage of customers who settle their accounts within 21 days.

(J.M.B.)

13. Draw a cumulative frequency polygon for the grouped frequency distribution:

Millimetres of rain	Number of years
500–549	1
550–599	10
600–649	8
650–699	5
700–799	4
800–899	2

Use your graph to estimate (a) the median, (b) the twentieth and the eightieth percentiles, and (c) the number of years for which the annual rainfall was between 625 mm and 775 mm.

The annual rainfalls, in millimetres, during the immediately preceding ten years were respectively

708,   695,   587,   543,   583,   551,   784,   638,   578,   583.

Estimate the median annual rainfall for the combined period of forty years.

(J.M.B.)

14. The following table shows the grouped frequency distribution of the hectarage under crops and grass for 200 farms in a certain geographical region.

Hectarage	Number of farms
Under 5	8
5– under 10	25
10– under 30	44
30– under 50	38
50– under 100	48
100– under 150	20
150– under 300	12
300 or more	5

(a) Draw, on a sheet of graph paper, the cumulative frequency polygon for the distribution.
(b) Determine the median and the quartiles of the distribution.
(c) Determine the hectarage under crops and grass which is exceeded by 30 per cent of the farms in the region.

(J.M.B.)

15. In a cookery competition 190 girls took part in the first round and the cumulative frequency distribution for the points awarded is as follows:

Score less than	9.5	19.5	29.5	39.5	49.5	59.5	69.5	79.5	89.5
Cumulative frequency	0	5	27	64	117	149	170	182	190

How many girls had a score in the range 40–49 points?

Draw the ogive and obtain an estimate of the median score from it. Obtain an estimate of the median score by calculation.

What score is likely to be required to qualify for the next round if the top 30 girls are to be selected?

(N.I.)

16. A group of 60 girls had their heights recorded correct to the nearest cm. The following results were obtained:

Height exceeding	115	125	135	145	155
Number of girls	60	56	45	18	5

Estimate the number of girls with heights greater than 140 cm.

17. An analysis of 500 sentences in a certain book gave the following results:

Number of words per sentence	Number of sentences
1–10	13
11–20	16
21–30	146
31–40	139
41–50	84
51–60	32
61 and above	20

Estimate
(a) the median,
(b) the percentage of sentences containing more than 45 words,
(c) the semi-interquartile range.
State the assumption upon which these estimates are based.

(A.E.B.)

18.

Weekly wage (£s)	10–	12–	15–	20–	30–50
Number of employees	22	64	55	36	23

The table gives the distribution of wages of employees in a small factory. What is the estimated percentage of the employees earning over £18?

(A.E.B.)

19. The masses of 400 men were measured to the nearest kilogram. Estimate the median mass from the grouped frequency table below.

Mass (kg)	Under 55	55–64	65–74	75–84	85–94	95 and over
Frequency	48	99	117	69	43	24

(A.E.B.)

20. If the lower and upper quartiles and the median of a distribution are 24, 41, and 32 respectively, what is the quartile deviation?
A. $8\frac{1}{2}$.
B. 17.
C. 34.
D. 8.

21. The table below shows the distribution of telephone calls through a particular exchange. Estimate the length of call above which 30 per cent of the calls lie.

Length of call (seconds)	Less than 30	30–	60–	120–	180–	240 and over
Frequency	7	35	70	50	17	17

22. A continuous variable, x, has the frequency curve shown in Figure 4.13. Sketch the corresponding cumulative frequency curve.

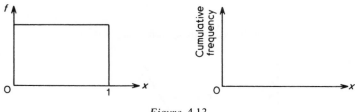

Figure 4.13

23. Sketch the cumulative frequency curve corresponding to the frequency curve shown in Figure 4.14.

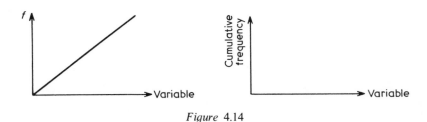

Figure 4.14

24. Sketch the frequency distribution corresponding to the cumulative frequency curve given below in Figure 4.15.

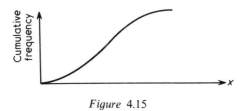

Figure 4.15

25. Sketch the cumulative frequency curve corresponding to the frequency distribution shown in Figure 4.16.

(A.E.B.)

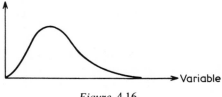

Figure 4.16

Answer to the problem at the end of the chapter (page 63):

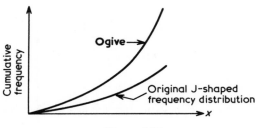

Figure 4.17

5
Measures of average, central tendency or location

5.1 Definitions of the mean, median, and mode

We have already mentioned in previous chapters that measures of average, for various reasons, are useful quantities. To begin with let us discuss the more important measures of average – the *mean, median,* and *mode* – and show how they may be calculated.

5.1.1 *The arithmetic mean (or the mean)*
There are several different means in statistics, e.g. the *arithmetic mean,* the *geometric mean,* the *harmonic mean,* etc., but normally when we use the term *mean* on its own we are referring to the *arithmetic mean.* In fact when we use the term *average* in every day speech, in the majority of cases we are signifying the arithmetic mean. For example, if someone says: 'On average I smoke 20 cigarettes a day', most of us would infer from this that in one week that person smoked about 140 cigarettes, although we would *not* expect them to have smoked precisely 20 cigarettes each day.

Most people have no difficulty in understanding the idea of an arithmetic mean, so let us now define it.

If we have a set of values: $x_1, x_2, x_3, x_4, \ldots, x_n$ for x, (i.e. n values altogether), then the *mean* $(\bar{x})$ of this set is given by:

$$\text{Mean}, \bar{x} = \frac{x_1 + x_2 + x_3 + x_4 + \ldots + x_n}{n}$$

There is a neater way of writing the above formula, *viz.*:

$$\bar{x} = \frac{\sum x}{n}$$

where $\sum x$ is a kind of mathematical shorthand instructing us to add up all the various x values. ($\sum$ is the Greek capital letter S (sigma) standing for Sum).

Example: In five consecutive innings a cricketer has the following scores: 24, 7, 184, 77, and 38. What is his average score?

$$\text{Average score} = \text{arithmetic mean score}$$

$$= \frac{24 + 7 + 184 + 77 + 38}{5}$$

$$= \frac{330}{5}$$

$$= 66$$

His average score is 66.

Question for the reader: would we obtain a different result if, in one of his innings, the batsman was not out?

There is, in certain cases, a very useful connection between the mean of one set of numbers and the mean of another related set. For example, if we know the mean of the numbers $x_1, x_2, x_3, \ldots, x_n$, we can *write down* the mean of a set of numbers such as $3x_1, 3x_2, 3x_3, \ldots, 3x_n$, or $(2x_1 - 1), (2x_2 - 1)$, $(2x_3 - 1), \ldots, (2x_n - 1)$.

If the mean of the set of numbers $x_1, x_2, x_3, \ldots, x_n$ is $\bar{x}$, it can be shown that $3x_1, 3x_2, 3x_3, \ldots, 3x_n$ has a mean of $3\bar{x}$, and that $(2x_1 - 1), (2x_2 - 1), (2x_3 - 1), \ldots,$ $(2x_n - 1)$ has a mean of $2\bar{x} - 1$.

In general, if the set of numbers $x_1, x_2, x_3, \ldots, x_n$ has a mean of $\bar{x}$, then the set of numbers $(mx_1 + a), (mx_2 + a), (mx_3 + a), \ldots, (mx_n + a)$ has a mean of $m\bar{x} + a$.

Proof: Let the set of numbers $x_1, x_-, x_3, \ldots, x_n$ have a mean of $\bar{x}$, that is

$$\frac{x_1 + x_2 + x_3 + \ldots + x_n}{n} = \bar{x}$$

or

$$\frac{\sum x}{n} = \bar{x}$$

Consider the set of numbers $(mx_1 + a), (mx_2 + a), (mx_3 + a), \ldots, (mx_n + a)$. Let their mean be $\bar{X}$, that is

$$\bar{X} = \frac{(mx_1 + a) + (mx_2 + a) + (mx_3 + a) + \ldots + (mx_n + a)}{n}$$

$$= \frac{(mx_1 + mx_2 + mx_3 + \ldots + mx_n) + na}{n}$$

$$= \frac{m(x_1 + x_2 + x_3 + \ldots + x_n) + na}{n}$$

$$= \frac{m\sum x + na}{n}$$

$$= m\frac{\sum x}{n} + a$$

$$= m\bar{x} + a$$

i.e. $\bar{X}$ equals $m\bar{x} + a$.

Examples: The numbers $1, 2, 3, 4,$ and 5 have a mean of 3, therefore:
(1) $4, 8, 12, 16,$ and 20 have a mean of $4 \times 3 = 12$.
(2) $6, 13, 20, 27,$ and 34 have a mean of $(7 \times 3) - 1 = 20$.

5.1.2 *The geometric mean*
If we have a set of x values: $x_1, x_2, x_3, x_4, \dots, x_n$ (i.e. n values altogether), we define their *geometric mean* as follows:

$$\text{Geometric mean} = \sqrt[n]{x_1 \times x_2 \times x_3 \times x_4 \times \dots \times x_n}$$

Thus, if we required the geometric mean of the five scores obtained by the cricketer (see example on page 72) then:

$$\text{Geometric mean} = \sqrt[n]{x_1 \times x_2 \times x_3 \times x_4 \times \dots \times x_n}$$

$$= \sqrt[5]{24 \times 7 \times 184 \times 77 \times 38}$$

$$= \sqrt[5]{90\,448\,512}$$

$$= 39.0 \text{ (correct to one decimal place)}$$

His geometric mean score is 39.0.

N.B. This is considerably less than his arithmetic mean score : 66.0.
In certain situations, for example where a quantity increases over equal intervals of time by a constant factor, the geometric mean will give us a much more realistic measure of average than the arithmetic mean.
For example, suppose a quantity is doubling in value every five years in the following manner:

Year 0	*Year 5*	*Year 10*
1000	2000	4000

Now, imagine that we know the values for Year 0 and Year 10 only and wish to *predict* the value for Year 5. Then, provided we know the quantity *is* increasing in the above manner, the geometric mean of the two values in question will give us the correct prediction for the value in Year 5, that is

$$\text{Value for Year 5} = \sqrt{1000 \times 4000}$$

$$= 2000.$$

N.B. The arithmetic mean would give us a value of 2500.

5.1.3   *The median*

We mentioned this quantity earlier when dealing with cumulative frequency tables and graphs. However, let us now look at it in the context of a set of numbers.

Suppose we start with just five x values which, *in ascending order of magnitude*, are x_1, x_2, x_3, x_4, and x_5. The *median* value is then x_3, for we define the median to be that value such that an equal number of the remaining values lie below and above it.

Let us look at the case where we have six x values. Suppose that in ascending order these are x_1, x_2, x_3, x_4, x_5, and x_6. What will be the median value in this case? The reader will probably see that we are in a quandary here, for there is no single central value. For instance, x_4 is clearly not the median, since three values lie below whilst only two lie above. Likewise, x_3 is no good on its own. The solution is fairly obvious: in the case where we have an *even* number of values, we bracket together the two central values (x_3 and x_4 in this case) and take the median to be the *mean* of these. Accordingly, the median in this example would be

$$\frac{(x_3 + x_4)}{2}$$

Example 1:   What is the median value of the five scores obtained by the cricketer in the example on page 72.

We have five scores: 24, 7, 184, 77, and 38. Putting these in ascending order (i.e. placing them in an array) we have:

$$7 \quad 24 \quad 38 \quad 77 \quad 184$$

The median score is clearly 38.

Example 2:   In his sixth innings the cricketer scores a duck (zero). What is his median score now?

We now have six scores: 24, 7, 184, 77, 38, and 0. Putting these into an array we have:

$$0 \quad 7 \quad 24 \quad 38 \quad 77 \quad 184.$$

Here the median will be:

$$\frac{24 + 38}{2} = 31$$

The median is 31.

5.1.4   *The mode*

This is an easy quantity to understand and to calculate. We define the *mode* of a set of numbers as that value which occurs most frequently. For example,

suppose we require to find the mode of the seven values: 15, 3, 11, 3, 19, 1, and 4.
Firstly, we put these into an array:

$$1 \quad 3 \quad 3 \quad 4 \quad 11 \quad 15 \quad 19$$

Clearly, the mode is 3.

N.B.   There can be more than one mode. For example, if we have the following array:

$$1 \quad 4 \quad 6 \quad 6 \quad 8 \quad 11 \quad 11 \quad 18$$

then, since 6 and 11 both occur *twice*, we have to say that there are *two* modes: 6 and 11.

A set of numbers having only one mode is said to be *unimodal*, a set of numbers having two modes is said to be *bimodal*, and so on.

5.2   Advantages and disadvantages of the mean, median, and mode

Having now mentioned several measures of average or location, let us look at these in slightly more detail and discuss their respective advantages and disadvantages.

5.2.1   *The mean*

One of the nightmares of a statistician is to come up with an 'average' value which is not really average at all! For example, suppose we measure the volumes of five glass flasks, all of which are supposed to have a volume of 250 cubic centimetres (cm^3), and find that in fact they have the following volumes: 249.3, 249.7, 258.4, 250.1, and 250.1 cm^3. Now, four of these values lie very close to the intended value of 250, whereas one value is way out. If we work out the mean of this sample, therefore, we are bound to get a distorted result, the distortion arising from the one value. This example illustrates both the advantage and the disadvantage of the mean as a measure of average: it has the advantage that *all* the values are used in its calculation, but it also has the disadvantage that one or two very low or very high values can seriously distort it.

In the above case, incidentally, the value of 258.4 is so far removed from the other values that we would probably regard it as a 'rogue' value, due perhaps to some malfunction in the machine making the flask, and using our common-sense we would tend to disregard it altogether. If we do this, we certainly get a more credible result: the mean of 249.3, 249.7, 258.4, 250.1, and 250.1 is 251.5; whereas the mean of 249.3, 249.7, 250.1, and 250.1 is 249.8.

One other advantage of the mean should perhaps be mentioned: most people do at least understand it, and since so much of statistics is concerned with the successful communication of data this in itself makes it an important quantity.

5.2.2   *The median*

In a way everything that can go wrong if we use the mean (see above) cannot go wrong if we use the median. For the median is *not* going to be affected by one or two 'rogue' values. Let us look at the volumes of the five flasks once more: their mean value is 251.5 cm^3. However, if we discard the value of 258.4 (as commonsense dictates), and find the mean of the remaining four values, we get 249.8. Let us see what we get if we work out the median of all five values:

$$249.3 \quad 249.7 \quad 250.1 \quad 250.1 \quad 258.4$$

The median value is 250.1, not so far removed from what we adjudge the mean to be (249.8) provided we discard our 'rogue' value.

The obvious advantage of the median is that we did not have to make any subjective judgment as to whether all the values were to be included or not. A disadvantage is that only one or two values decide the median, namely the middle ones; none of the other values are used and for this reason it can be argued that the median can never be truly representative.

5.2.3   *The mode*
The properties of the mode are intermediate between those of the mean and the median. Thus, although the mode is calculated from several values in a set and is therefore normally more representative than the median, not all the values are used so it will be much less representative than the mean.

As for distortion, the mode is much less likely to be influenced by extreme values than is the mean, but it is still inferior to the median in this respect.

If we look once again at the five values:

$$249.3 \quad 249.7 \quad 250.1 \quad 250.1 \quad 258.4,$$

then the mode is, of course, 250.1, which compares favourably with the mean based on four values only (249.8) and the median (250.1). However, it should be pointed out that we might have been unlucky, e.g. suppose we had obtained the following as our five values:

$$249.3 \quad 249.7 \quad 250.1 \quad 258.4 \quad 258.4$$

and did not realize that the two 258.4s were likely to be 'rogue' values. Then for the *mode* we would get 258.4, for the *mean* (using all five values) we would get 253.2, and only for the *median* would we *still* get a reasonable value, i.e. 250.1.

To summarize then, it can be seen that none of these measures of average is always satisfactory in all circumstances.

5.3   Calculating the mean, median, and mode from a grouped frequency distribution

5.3.1   *The mean*
Suppose that instead of a set of numbers we are confronted with a Grouped Frequency Distribution—how are we now to calculate the *mean*? Firstly, we have to make some assumptions which means that the value we obtain will nearly always be approximate. Let us consider the following table, involving a continuous variable, and proceed from there.

Class	Frequency
0–10	1
10–20	3
20–30	8
30–40	22
40–50	9
50–60	5
60–70	2

Consider for a moment the fifth class: we have 9 values in it lying between 40 and 50. If we make the assumption that these 9 values are spread evenly throughout, then their mean value will be about half-way between the lower and upper boundaries of this particular class—their mean is therefore about 45. Thus, we can think of the class 40–50 as contributing 9 values of 45 and, of course, we can argue in a similar way for the other six classes.

Accordingly, the first step is to take the original table and add a column of *mid-class values* (these are sometimes, somewhat misleadingly, referred to as 'class-marks'):

Class	Mid-class value, x	Frequency, f
0–10	5	1
10–20	15	3
20–30	25	8
30–40	35	22
40–50	45	9
50–60	55	5
60–70	65	2

What then is the mean? Well, the first class gives us 1 value of 5, the second class gives us 3 values of 15, the third class gives us 8 values of 25, and so on, so if we think in terms of a set of numbers for a moment, we have to work out the mean of 5, 15, 15, 15, 25, 25, 25, 25, 25, 25, 25, 25, ... , 65, 65.

The mean therefore is

$\sum x/n = [5 + (15 + 15 + 15) + (25 + 25 + 25 + 25 + 25 + 25 + 25 + 25) +$
$... + (65 + 65)] \div$ (the total number of values).

But the total number of values is clearly $1 + 3 + 8 + ... + 2$, and so the mean is equal to:

$$\frac{1 \times 5 + 3 \times 15 + 8 \times 25 ... + 2 \times 65}{1 + 3 + 8 ... + 2}$$

The mean is given the symbol $\bar{x}$, and if we think of the mid-class values as being 'x' values (with $x_1 = 5, x_2 = 15$, etc.) and the frequency values as being 'f' values (with $f_1 = 1, f_2 = 3$, etc.), then we have the following formula:

$$\text{mean, } \bar{x} = \frac{f_1 \times x_1 + f_2 \times x_2 + f_3 \times x_3 + \dots + f_7 \times x_7}{f_1 + f_2 + f_3 + \dots + f_7}$$

or

$$\bar{x} = \frac{f_1 x_1 + f_2 x_2 + f_3 x_3 + \dots + f_7 x_7}{f_1 + f_2 + f_3 + \dots + f_7}$$

It is quite sufficient if the reader uses the above formula, but there is a neater way of expressing it, as follows:

$$\bar{x} = \frac{\text{the sum of all the individual } fxs}{\text{the sum of all the individual } fs}$$

and mathematically this can be written:

$$\bar{x} = \frac{\sum fx}{\sum f}$$

Let us now work out the arithmetic mean for the above data, correct to one decimal place:

$$\text{mean, } \bar{x} = \frac{\sum fx}{\sum f}$$

$$= \frac{1 \times 5 + 3 \times 15 + 8 \times 25 + 22 \times 35 + 9 \times 45 + 5 \times 55 + 2 \times 65}{1 + 3 + 8 + 22 + 9 + 5 + 2}$$

i.e.

$$\bar{x} = \frac{1830}{50}$$

$$\Rightarrow \bar{x} = 36.60$$

The mean is approximately 36.6.

If the frequency distribution involves a discrete variable then, again making the assumption that values are spread evenly across classes, the mid-class values are now obtained by averaging the lowest and highest values permitted for each class; e.g. classes 0–9, 10–19, 20–29, ..., 60–69 would have mid-class values of 4.5, 14.5, 24.5, ..., 64.5.

When the grouped frequency distribution is an awkward one, i.e. has unequal class-widths and/or some 'open-ended' classes, then we have to proceed more carefully. For example, consider the hypothetical data in the following table.

A little thought will show that we are in no particular difficulty about classes 2–5, despite their varying class-widths, and in fact we just assign to each of these the appropriate mid-class values, as shown in the second table.

	Class	Frequency
1.	Under 20	4
2.	20–30	9
3.	30–50	62
4.	50–55	10
5.	55–60	8
6.	Over 60	7

	Class	Mid-class value, x	Frequency, f
1.	Under 20	15	4
2.	20–30	25	9
3.	30–50	40	62
4.	50–55	$52\frac{1}{2}$	10
5.	55–60	$57\frac{1}{2}$	8
6.	Over 60	?	7

However, what about the two open-ended classes 1 and 7? What mid-class value are we to assign to them? Obviously we will have to make assumptions about (a) the likely or sensible lower limit for the class 'Under 20' and (b) the likely or sensible upper limit for the class 'Over 60'. Very often the nature of the data itself will help us decide, but it must be emphasized that they will *only* be estimates. Now, supposing the above data relates to the examination marks of 100 candidates; then, for the class 'Under 20' we could substitute '10–20' say, on the assumption that it is rather unlikely that any candidate will have scored less than 10. Likewise for the class 'over 60' we could substitute '60–80' say, again on the assumption that it is unlikely (for this particular distribution) that any candidate will have scored over 80. Having made these assumptions we then obtain the following:

Class	Mid-class value, x	Frequency, f
Under 20 → 10–20	15	4
20–30	25	9
30–50	40	62
50–55	$52\frac{1}{2}$	10
55–60	$57\frac{1}{2}$	8
Over 60 → 60–80	70	7

The reader should now work out the mean of the above distribution to one decimal place. (For the answer see page 87.) Remember that you have now made several assumptions in order to calculate this value.

5.3.2   *The median*
The calculation of the median from a grouped frequency distribution has already been dealt with in Chapter 4. However, there is nothing like practice! As a useful revision exercise the reader should now calculate the median of the above data. (For the answer see page 87.)

5.3.3   *The mode*
It is possible to calculate the mode of a grouped frequency distribution, but it does involve a fairly difficult calculation and it is probably easier if we firstly explain how the mode can be obtained diagrammatically. Suppose from some distribution or other we have obtained the histogram shown in Figure 5.1.

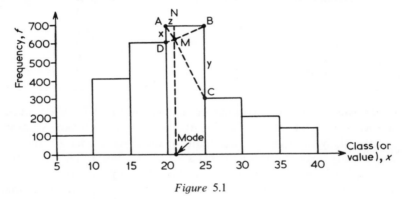

Figure 5.1

The class 20–25, incidentally, is called the *modal class*, because it is the class of highest frequency.

Now, the only parts of the histogram in Figure 5.1 we need concern ourselves with are the points A, B, C, and D. A and B are at either end of the top of the tallest rectangle, while C and D are the points of contact between the latter and the tops of the two adjacent rectangles. The mode is then found as illustrated on Figure 5.1, i.e. considering the quadrilateral ABCD, we join up the two diagonals AC and BD noting where they cross at M. A vertical line down from M onto the *Class* axis then yields the modal value – about 22 in this case.

Suppose, however, we wish to *calculate* the mode. From Figure 5.1 it is clear that we need to know AN and we proceed to find this as follows. If AD = x and BC = y, it can be shown that MN is $\dfrac{xy}{x+y}$. From Figure 5.1,

$$x = 100 \text{ and } y = 400$$

so

$$MN = \frac{100 \times 400}{100 + 400}$$

$$= 80$$

Now, the triangles AMN and ACB are similar and it therefore follows that:

$$\frac{AN}{AB} = \frac{MN}{CB}$$

since $AB = 5$, we have

$$\frac{AN}{5} = \frac{80}{400}$$

$$\Rightarrow AN = 1$$

Therefore,

$$\text{mode} = (20 + AN)$$

$$= 20 + 1$$

$$= 21$$

By calculation the mode is 21.

Note that our calculated value (21.0) compares well with the diagrammatic value (22).

5.4 Calculating the mean, median, and mode from a discrete frequency distribution

A discrete frequency distribution, as already mentioned, deals with the frequencies of various values of a discrete variable. For example, an importer might make a check on say 35 crates of oranges and list the number of crates f, containing $0, 1, 2, \ldots$, etc. bad oranges, x, with the following results:

x	f
0	4
1	7
2	9
3	8
4	6
5	1
	35

The above table shows that the importer found 4 crates with no bad oranges, 7 crates with 1 bad orange, and so on. Now, the question may arise as to how we are to calculate the mean, median, and mode of such a distribution, so let us deal with them in order.

5.4.1 *The mean*
To all intents and purposes we calculate this in exactly the same way as we

did for a grouped frequency distribution. Our 'x' values are no longer mid-class values, of course, but our 'f' values have the same significance as before.

Accordingly, the mean, $\bar{x}$, is obtained by using the formula:

$$\bar{x} = \frac{\sum fx}{\sum f}$$

So, for the above data:

$$\bar{x} = \frac{4 \times 0 + 7 \times 1 + 9 \times 2 + 8 \times 3 + 6 \times 4 + 1 \times 5}{4 + 7 + 9 + 8 + 6 + 1}$$

$$= 2.2$$

(correct to one decimal place)

The mean is 2.2.

5.4.2   The median
To find the median it is generally easier to construct a cumulative frequency table first, for the median can then usually be found by inspection; i.e. we have:

x	f	Cumulative frequency
0	4	4
1	7	11
2	9	20
3	8	28
4	6	34
5	1	35

There are 35 values altogether, so we require to know the eighteenth. Since there are 11 values of 1 or less, and 20 values of 2 or less, the median is clearly 2 (18 lying between 11 and 20).

The median is 2.

5.4.3   The mode
This can normally be found by inspection of the original frequency distribution. In this case, the most frequently occurring value is 2 (it occurs 9 times).

The mode is 2.

Finally, in order to help in the understanding of the various measures of average, a short exercise follows. There are five statements and in each of them the word average is used. The reader should try and decide in each case whether it refers to the mean, the median or the mode.

(1) On average, people in Britain eat one egg for breakfast.
(2) The average number of children per family in this country is 2.3.
(3) In this college half the students are of above average intelligence.
(4) A person selected at random in this country is almost certain to have more than the average number of fingers.
(5) The average barrister earns more than the average solicitor.
(For the answer see page 87.)

Exercise 5

1. Calculate for the following numbers

    26,   21,   28,   22,   23,   27,   23,   25,   23,   24,

    (a) the arithmetic mean,
    (b) the median,
    (c) the mode.

2. The mean of three numbers is 15, whilst the mean of these and another two numbers is 28. If one of the latter is 20, what is the other?

3. Find the median of

    10,   17,   5,   18,   2,   17,   19,   and 13.

    (A.E.B.)

4. Find the mean of the n integers $1, 2, 3, \ldots, n$.

    (A.E.B.)

5. What is the mode of the following set of numbers?

    4   7   11   14   16   16   31

    (A.E.B.)

6. The population of a certain town was 18 000 in 1951 and 36 000 in 1971. Calculate the *geometric* mean of the two populations, giving your answer correct to the nearest thousand. Outline the circumstances under which the geometric mean would give a better estimate for the population of the town in 1961 than the arithmetic mean.

    (A.E.B.)

7. The arithmetic mean of a set of n numbers is
    A. The middle number.
    B. The number that occurs most frequently.
    C. $\dfrac{n+1}{2}$.
    D. The sum of the numbers divided by n.

8. Find, for the following set of numbers, the mean, median, and mode:

    9   8   12   12   16   15   14   5   10   10   6   12

    (Give your answers correct to one decimal place.)

9. The pupils of a class are given ten tests in arithmetic during a school term. After nine of the tests the marks of a particular pupil are:

    6,   7,   5,   8,   6,   5,   4,   6,   9.

(a) State the mode of these marks.

(b) Find the median of these marks.

(c) After the tenth test, the arithmetic mean and the median of this pupil's marks are equal. How many marks did the pupil get for the last test?

(J.M.B.)

10. (a) Calculate the mean of the numbers 1, 4, 7, 11, and 12.

(b) Write down the mean of the numbers 8, 32, 56, 88, and 96.

(c) Write down the mean of the numbers 3, 21, 39, 63, and 69.

11. If the mean of the numbers $x_1, x_2, \ldots, x_n$ is 7, find the mean of

(a) $5x_1, 5x_2, \ldots, 5x_n$.

(b) $3x_1 - 2, 3x_2 - 2, \ldots, 3x_n - 2$.

(A.E.B.)

12. Some pupils in a class are being taught to use a new type of weighing machine. Seven boys each weigh the same object and their readings are recorded in grams as follows:

$$12.4, \quad 12.7, \quad 19.2, \quad 12.5, \quad 12.4, \quad 12.6, \quad 12.7.$$

Calculate the arithmetic mean of this set of values. Explain why this value of the mean is likely to be greater than the correct weight of the object and obtain a better estimate to the correct value.

(N.I.)

13. Give two disadvantages of the mode as a measure of position.

(A.E.B.)

14.

Class	Frequency
0 and up to 2	176
2 and up to 10	222
10 and up to 20	343
20 and up to 30	285
30 and up to 40	312
40 and up to 50	306
50 and up to 60	296
60 and up to 70	182
70 and up to 80	100
80 and up to 110	28

For the above table calculate:

(a) the arithmetic mean and

(b) the median,

(Give your answers correct to one decimal place.)

15. The marks obtained by 100 candidates were distributed as follows:

Mark	0–19	20–29	30–39	40–49	50–59	60–69	70–79	80–99
Number of candidates	3	9	17	25	27	10	5	4

Estimate the arithmetic mean.

16. The table below gives the monthly wages of 100 employees

Monthly wages(£)	Frequency
50 +	3
60 +	9
70 +	17
80 +	25
90 +	27
100 +	10
120–180	9
Total	100

(a) State the mid-value of each class interval of the distribution and draw the histogram.
(b) Find diagrammatically the mode of the distribution.
(c) Calculate the mode of the distribution.

17.

Age (years)	10–	11–	12–	13–	14–	15–	16–
Frequency	100	92	90	85	90	95	80

The table above shows the distribution of the ages of pupils in a school. What is the frequency of the modal group?
A. 80.
B. 85.
C. 90.
D. 100.

18. The floor area of houses on a particular estate was calculated correct to the nearest square metre, and the results are given below.

Floor area (m^2)	Cumulative frequency
20– 39	7
40– 59	23
60– 79	65
80– 99	139
100–119	212
120–139	253
140–159	272
160–179	284
180–199	292
200–259	300

Calculate
(a) the mid-class values,
(b) the frequency of each class,
(c) the arithmetic mean of the distribution.

19. The following table shows the grouped frequency distribution of the annual rainfall, recorded to the nearest mm, at a weather station over a period of thirty years.

Rainfall (mm)	500–549	550–599	600–649	650–699	700–799	800–899
Number of years	1	10	8	5	4	2

(a) Exhibit the distribution as a histogram.

(b) Estimate the mean annual rainfall.

(c) Given that the mean annual rainfall for the immediately preceding ten years was 625 mm, estimate the mean annual rainfall for the combined period of forty years.

(J.M.B.)

20. Estimate the mode of the following distribution both diagrammatically and by calculation.

Length (cm)	0–	5–	10–	15–	20 and over
Frequency	8	12	6	3	1

(A.E.B.)

21. The following table shows the size (in hectares) and the frequency (to the nearest 100) of vineyards in a certain Department of France:

Size (hectares)	Frequency
0– 10	5500
10– 20	4100
20– 40	3900
40– 80	3200
80– 160	2400
160–1280	700

State which of the mean, median or mode is the most appropriate measure of position to use with the above data. Give reasons for your choice and estimate the measure you select.

22.

Mark	2	3	4	5	6	7	8	9	10
Number of pupils	1	6	6	9	14	21	11	10	2

The table gives the distribution of marks in a test. What is the mean mark obtained?

(A.E.B.)

23.

Number of days	0–	50–	100–	150–	200–	250–	300–365	Total
Number of children	29	24	30	20	25	17	11	156

The table gives the ages in days (over 15 years) of children in the fifth form at a particular school. What is the median age of children in the fifth form at that school?

(A.E.B.)

24. Determine the median of the following discrete frequency distribution:

Value, x	0	1	2	3	4	5	6	7
Frequency, f	39	22	19	12	5	1	1	1

25. The table below shows the number of calls per day received at a fire station over a given period. Calculate the mean number of calls per day.

Number of calls per day	0	1	2	3	4	5
Number of days	75	62	32	16	9	6

(A.E.B.)

26. The number of bracts on specimens of a particular species of plant are tabulated below. Determine the mode.

Number of bracts	4	5	6	7	8	9	10	11	12	13	14	15
Number of specimens	1	1	1	2	12	10	6	6	2	2	1	1

(A.E.B.)

27. The table below shows the number of calls per day received by a fire station over a given year. Determine the median of this distribution.

Number of calls per day	0	1	2	3	4	5	6 and over
Number of days	139	102	57	30	19	12	6

(A.E.B.)

28. In an attempt to compare the standards of referees in a football league, the referee is given a grade from 0 to 6 by the secretary of each of the home and away teams after each match. The table below shows the distribution of the grades given to a particular referee after 4 matches:

Grade	0	1	2	3	4	5	6
Frequency	1	0	3	2	0	0	2

State the mode of the grades.

After one further match the mean of all the grades for this referee was still the same as it was after 4 matches. If the secretary of the home team gave a grade of 5, what grade did the secretary of the away team give?

(J.M.B.)

29. An electronic device is made from three components, one each of types A, B, and C. Components of each type are produced by several manufacturers, the prices being shown below.

	Type A	£3, £4, £4, £5
Component	Type B	£12, £14, £15
	Type C	£1, £1, £1, £2

Draw up a frequency table of the cost of the 48 possible ways of purchasing the necessary components. Use this table to obtain the arithmetic mean for this distribution.

(A.E.B.)

Answers to the problems in Chapter 5:
page 80 (mean) : 42.4
page 80 (median) : 41.9
page 83 : (1) mode, (2) mean, (3) median, (4) mean, (5) median.

6
Measures of dispersion or spread

The ideas of average and spread with regard to a statistical distribution have already been briefly mentioned in earlier chapters. To recap: measures of average or central tendency, as their name implies, give us some idea of the size of central values, while measures of spread or dispersion give us some idea of how the values of a distribution cluster around the average; i.e. diagrammatically (for a 'normal' distribution):

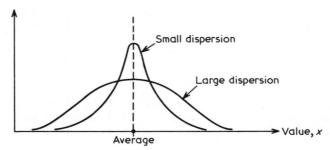

Figure 6.1

N.B. Total area beneath both curves is equal.

As can be seen from Figure 6.1, if the dispersion is small many values cluster around the average (and approximate to it), whereas if the dispersion is large a considerable proportion of values are markedly different from the average. Incidentally, the importance of measures of average, such as the mean, and measures of dispersion, such as the standard deviation, can be appreciated when it is realized that for all normally distributed variables, be they discrete or continuous, approximately 68 per cent of the values lie within one standard deviation (S.D.) of the mean, approximately 95 per cent within two S.D.s and practically 100 per cent within three S.D.s.

Let us now examine various quantities which can give us a measure of dispersion.

6.1 The range

The *range* of a distribution is simply the difference between the two extreme items, i.e. it is the difference between the highest value and the lowest value. In Figure 6.1, it can be seen that, in general, a small dispersion means a small range, while a large dispersion means a large range. The range, therefore, can often give us a good idea of the dispersion. Now, if we have a set of numbers and require their range, it will obviously be helpful if we first put them into an array, that is arrange them in order from low to high.

Question: Find the range of the following set of numbers:

$$3 \quad 9 \quad 17 \quad 27 \quad 1 \quad 4 \quad 23 \quad 19 \quad 5$$

(For the answer to this question see page 111.)

If we have a grouped frequency distribution, without details of all the individual values making up that distribution, then clearly we have to make some assumptions. For instance suppose we have the following:

Class	Frequency
$-\frac{1}{2} - +\frac{1}{2}$	1
$\frac{1}{2} - 1\frac{1}{2}$	12
$1\frac{1}{2} - 2\frac{1}{2}$	18
$2\frac{1}{2} - 3\frac{1}{2}$	24
$3\frac{1}{2} - 4\frac{1}{2}$	6
$4\frac{1}{2} - 5\frac{1}{2}$	3

What is the range in this case? Obviously, the highest value must lie somewhere in the highest class of $4\frac{1}{2}-5\frac{1}{2}$, and since there are three values, it is probably a reasonable assumption that one is a 'low' value (i.e. $\simeq 4\frac{1}{2}$), one a 'medium' value (i.e. ≥ 5), and one a 'high' value (i.e. $\simeq 5\frac{1}{2}$); therefore, we could take $5\frac{1}{2}$ to be the highest value. Similarly, the lowest value must lie somewhere in the lowest class, but since there is only one value here, it would clearly be unreasonable to suppose that it is necessarily either a 'low' or a 'high' value. The best we can do is to assume that it will be a 'medium' value. Accordingly, we can take the lowest value to be 0. The range is therefore about $5\frac{1}{2} - 0 = 5\frac{1}{2}$ in this case.

N.B. If we require the range of a discrete frequency distribution we merely treat it as an array, i.e. if the discrete variable x takes values 0, 1, 2, 3, and 4, its range is clearly 4 (4−0).

6.2 The semi-interquartile range

This quantity has already been mentioned in Chapter 4, and we will now try and explain why it can give us a measure of dispersion. Suppose we have a distribution with a low dispersion, then we would expect a large proportion of the values to be close to the central or average value. If for the latter we consider the median, then the lower quartile, Q_1, must lie relatively close to it in this case, since only 25 per cent of the values lie below. Similarly, the upper quartile, Q_3, must lie relatively close to the median. Now, we define the *semi-interquartile range* (S.I.R.) as:

$$\text{S.I.R.} = \frac{Q_3 - Q_1}{2}$$

and clearly if Q_3 and Q_1 are both close to the median, they are both relatively close to each other. Accordingly, $Q_3 - Q_1$ is going to be small, and we should expect the S.I.R. to be small. For a large dispersion exactly the opposite will apply.

To summarize then: a low S.I.R. generally means a small dispersion, while a high S.I.R. generally means a large dispersion.

Question: Calculate the semi-interquartile range of the distribution given on page 89.
(For the answer to this question see page 111.)

We can also explain diagrammatically why the S.I.R. is a measure of dispersion. The area beneath a frequency distribution curve is directly proportional to the frequency itself, and therefore a vertical line representing the median will,

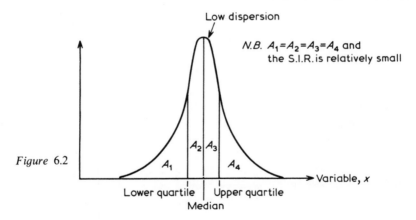

Figure 6.2

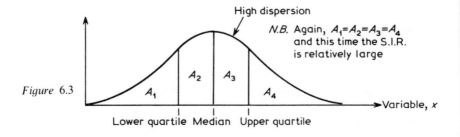

Figure 6.3

by definition, divide such a curve into two *equal* areas. Similarly, the two quartiles together with the median will divide such a curve into four equal areas. We have marked these quantities on two distributions: one of low dispersion (Figure 6.2) and one of high dispersion (Figure 6.3).

It can be seen that a low dispersion goes with a low S.I.R., and vice versa.

6.3   Inter-percentile ranges

An *inter-percentile range* is yet another measure of dispersion, for the same sort of reason that the S.I.R. is. In fact the S.I.R. is closely related to an inter-percentile range, for the lower quartile is, of course, the same as the 25th percentile and the upper quartile is the same as the 75th percentile. It follows, therefore, that the '25–75' inter-percentile range will be *twice* the semi-interquartile range. Note that, in general, the lower and upper limits of any particular inter-percentile range will be at equal distances from the median (the 50th percentile). Accordingly, we talk about the '20–80' or the '30–70' inter-percentile range. Very commonly used is the '40–60'. Again, it is a useful exercise to calculate the '40–60' inter-percentile range of the frequency distribution given on page 89. This time we will do it as a worked example.

Example: Calculate the '40–60' inter-percentile range of the following grouped frequency distribution:

Class	Frequency
$-\frac{1}{2} - +\frac{1}{2}$	1
$\frac{1}{2} - 1\frac{1}{2}$	12
$1\frac{1}{2} - 2\frac{1}{2}$	18
$2\frac{1}{2} - 3\frac{1}{2}$	24
$3\frac{1}{2} - 4\frac{1}{2}$	6
$4\frac{1}{2} - 5\frac{1}{2}$	3

The cumulative frequency distribution is therefore:

Class	Cumulative frequency	Frequency
$-\frac{1}{2} - +\frac{1}{2}$	1	1
$\frac{1}{2} - 1\frac{1}{2}$	13	12
$1\frac{1}{2} - 2\frac{1}{2}$	31	18
$2\frac{1}{2} - 3\frac{1}{2}$	55	24
$3\frac{1}{2} - 4\frac{1}{2}$	61	6
$4\frac{1}{2} - 5\frac{1}{2}$	64	3

For the 40th percentile we require the $(\frac{40}{100} \times 64)$th value of the distribution which is the 25.6th value. Similarly, for the 60th percentile we require the $(\frac{60}{100} \times 64)$th value, or the 38.4th.

$$\text{The 25.6th value} = 1.5 + \frac{12.6}{18} \times 1 = 2.2$$

$$\text{The 38.4th value} = 2.5 + \frac{7.4}{24} \times 1 = 2.8$$

Therefore:

$$\begin{aligned}\text{The '40--60' inter-percentile range} &= \text{60th percentile} - \text{40th percentile} \\ &= 2.8 - 2.2 \\ &= 0.6\end{aligned}$$

The '40–60' inter-percentile range is 0.6.

6.4 The mean deviation

Let us first define this term, confining ourselves for the moment to a set of numbers. As the name implies it is the *mean* of a series of *deviations*. Deviations from what? In fact, usually deviations from the mean. Let us illustrate exactly how the *mean deviation* of a set of numbers is computed, using for our set the numbers in the question on page 89, *viz.*:

$$3 \quad 9 \quad 17 \quad 27 \quad 1 \quad 4 \quad 23 \quad 19 \quad 5$$

First, find the mean:

$$\bar{x} = \tfrac{108}{9}$$
$$= 12$$

Now, write down the deviation of each value from the mean of 12, regarding all deviations as being *positive*, (something quite unjustified mathematically!):

Value, x	3	9	17	27	1	4	23	19	5
Deviation, d	9	3	5	15	11	8	11	7	7

N.B. $d = |x - \bar{x}|$.

Now, the mean deviation, M.D., is given by:

$$\frac{d_1 + d_2 + d_3 + \ldots + d_n}{n}$$

where n is the number of values in the set, or

$$\text{M.D.} = \frac{\sum d}{n}$$

so here

$$\text{M.D.} = \frac{9 + 3 + 5 + \ldots + 7}{9}$$

$$= \tfrac{76}{9}$$

$$= 8.4 \text{ recurring.}$$

The mean deviation is 8.4 (correct to one decimal place).

From the formula $\dfrac{\sum d}{n}$, it can be seen why the mean deviation gives us another measure of dispersion. For, if we have a set of numbers having a high dispersion, many values will differ considerably from the mean and accordingly $\sum d$ will be *large*. Therefore, the mean deviation (M.D.) will be large. The converse is also true.

To summarize then: a small M.D. means a low dispersion, while a large M.D. means a high dispersion.

6.5   The mean deviation from the median

Sometimes the mean deviation is calculated not from the mean but from the *median*. The method of calculation is very similar, of course, and can be illustrated with reference to the set of numbers just used:

we have   3   9   17   27   1   4   23   19   5

which put into an ascending array gives:

1   3   4   5   9   17   19   23   27

therefore, the median is 9.

We again write down the deviation of each value, this time from the median, again regarding all deviations as being positive:

Value, x	1	3	4	5	9	17	19	23	27
Deviation (d') from median	8	6	5	4	0	8	10	14	18

M.D. from median $= \dfrac{\sum d'}{n}$

so here

$$\text{M.D.} = \frac{8+6+5\ldots+18}{9}$$

$$= \tfrac{73}{9}$$

$$= 8.1 \text{ recurring}$$

The mean deviation from the median is 8.1 (correct to one decimal place).

The mean deviation from the median gives us a measure of dispersion for precisely the same reason that the mean deviation from the mean does.

6.6   The standard deviation

Like the mean, the *standard deviation* is a quantity of fundamental importance in statistics. Once again, as its name implies, it is concerned with deviations, and, in fact, these are deviations from the *mean*. Accordingly, if we require the *standard deviation* of a set of numbers, we must first compute the mean. We next write down the deviation, d, of each number, x, from the mean, $\bar{x}$, giving each d an appropriate algebraic sign (i.e. $+$ or $-$). We then compute the corresponding *square*, d^2. Finally, we work out the mean of our 'squared deviations', and take the square-root—this gives us the standard deviation. Let us get straight down to a worked example.

Example: Calculate the standard deviation of the numbers:

$$3 \quad 9 \quad 17 \quad 27 \quad 1 \quad 4 \quad 23 \quad 19 \quad 5$$

giving the answer correct to one decimal place.

$$\text{mean, } \bar{x} = \frac{3 + 9 + 17 + 27 + 1 + 4 + 23 + 19 + 5}{9}$$

$$= 12$$

We can now compile the following table:

Number, x	Deviation, d	Deviation squared, d^2
3	-9	81
9	-3	9
17	$+5$	25
27	$+15$	225
1	-11	121
4	-8	64
23	$+11$	121
19	$+7$	49
5	-7	49
		$\sum d^2 = 744$

N.B. $d = x - \bar{x}$, and here, $\bar{x} = 12$

The standard deviation, s is given by:

$$\sqrt{\frac{d_1^2 + d_2^2 + d_3^2 + \ldots + d_n^2}{n}}$$

where n is the number of values in the set, or

$$s = \sqrt{\frac{\sum d^2}{n}}$$

so here

$$s = \sqrt{\frac{81 + 9 + 225 + 121 + 64 + 121 + 49 + 49}{9}}$$

$$= \sqrt{\frac{744}{9}}$$

$$= 9.092$$

The standard deviation is 9.1 (correct to one decimal place).

There is, in certain cases, a very useful connection between the standard deviations of one set of numbers and another. For example, if we know the standard deviation of the numbers $x_1, x_2, x_3, \ldots, x_n$, we can *write down* the standard deviation of a set of numbers such as $2x_1, 2x_2, 2x_3, \ldots, 2x_n$, or $(3x_1 + 1)$, $(3x_2 + 1), (3x_3 + 1), \ldots, (3x_n + 1)$. In fact, if the standard deviation of the set of numbers $x_1, x_2, x_3, \ldots, x_n$ is s, it can be shown that $2x_1, 2x_2, 2x_3, \ldots, 2x_n$ has a standard deviation of $2s$, and that $(3x_1 + 1), (3x_2 + 1), (3x_3 + 1), \ldots, (3x_n + 1)$ has a standard deviation of $3s$.

In general, if the set of numbers $x_1, x_2, x_3, \ldots, x_n$ has a standard deviation of s, then the set of numbers $(mx_1 + a), (mx_2 + a), (mx_3 + a), \ldots, (mx_n + a)$ has a standard deviation of ms.

Proof: Let the set of numbers $x_1, x_2, x_3, \ldots, x_n$ have a mean of $\bar{x}$ and a standard deviation of s:
i.e.

$$s = \sqrt{\frac{\sum (x - \bar{x})^2}{n}}$$

Now, consider the set of numbers $(mx_1 + a), (mx_2 + a), (mx_3 + a), \ldots, (mx_n + a)$. Let their mean be $\bar{X}$ and their standard deviation be S; i.e.

$$S = \sqrt{\frac{\sum [(mx + a) - \bar{X}]^2}{n}}$$

but, $\bar{X} = m\bar{x} + a$ (see proof on page 72), so:

$$S = \sqrt{\frac{\sum [mx + a - m\bar{x} - a]^2}{n}}$$

$$= \sqrt{\frac{\sum (mx - m\bar{x})^2}{n}}$$

$$= \sqrt{\frac{\sum m^2(x - \bar{x})^2}{n}}$$

$$= \sqrt{\frac{m^2 \sum (x - \bar{x})^2}{n}} ;$$

i.e.

$$S = m\sqrt{\frac{(x - \bar{x})^2}{n}}$$

$$= ms$$

i.e. S equals ms.

Examples: The numbers 6, 7, 8, 9, and 10 have a standard deviation of 1.4; therefore (1) the numbers 18, 21, 24, 27, and 30 will have a standard deviation of $3 \times 1.4 = 4.2$.

(2)   The numbers 28, 33, 38, 43, and 48 will have a standard deviation of $5 \times 1.4 = 7.0$.

N.B. $28 = (5 \times 6) - 2$, $33 = (5 \times 7) - 2$, etc.

Again, it is fairly self-evident why the standard deviation gives us a measure of dispersion. If the numbers themselves vary markedly from the mean, there will be some relatively large values for d and consequently for d^2. $\sum d^2$ will therefore be large, making the standard deviation itself large. Once again, therefore, a high value for the standard deviation means a large dispersion, a low value means a small dispersion.

In contrast to the two mean deviations, the standard deviation is mathematically sound, since the difficulty over positive or negative deviations is neatly avoided by squaring them all, thereby ensuring that we always have positive quantities to deal with.

Just as the mean is often given the symbol $\bar{x}$, so the standard deviation, as already indicated above, is often given the symbol s.

6.7   The variance

The *variance* is simply the square of the standard deviation. The formula for the variance of a set of numbers is, therefore:

$$\text{Variance} = \frac{\sum d^2}{n}$$

Logically, the variance is often given the symbol s^2. Clearly, for the set of numbers given above, $s^2 = 82.8$ (correct to one decimal place).

The variance is a quantity of great importance in advanced statistics, but can also prove very useful, in certain circumstances, in elementary statistics. For example, suppose we have two sets of numbers: set A and set B, *both having the same mean*. Set A comprises five numbers and has a S.D. of 4.4, whereas set B comprises seven numbers and has a S.D. of 4.9. What will be the S.D. if we now combine A and B into a single set of twelve numbers?

For   Set   A: S.D. $= 4.4$;   therefore   the   variance $= (4.4)^2 = 19.36$;   now variance $= \dfrac{\sum d^2}{n}$, so $\sum d^2 = n \times$ variance; therefore $\sum d_{\text{A}}^2 = 5 \times 19.36 = 96.80$

Similarly, for set $B : S.D. = 4.9$; so the variance $= 24.01$; therefore $\sum d_B^2 = 7 \times 24.01 = 168.07$.

The variance of the combined set will therefore be:

$$s^2 = \frac{96.80 + 168.07}{5 + 7}$$

$$= \frac{264.87}{12}$$

$$= 22.07$$

i.e. the variance, s^2, is 22.07.

The S.D. of the combined set is $\sqrt{22.07} = 4.7$ (correct to one decimal place).

The standard deviation, s, is 4.7.

N.B. The S.D. is *not* $\dfrac{5 \times 4.4 + 7 \times 4.9}{12}$.

6.8 Advantages and disadvantages of the various measures of dispersion

The range
Generally speaking the range is a reasonably good indication of dispersion, but it will be badly affected by just *one* extreme value—care is therefore necessary when it is used.

The semi-interquartile range
The S.I.R. has the advantage that is will not be affected by extreme values, however, it tells us nothing about the dispersion of a distribution beyond the quartiles.

Inter-percentile ranges
These, to a lesser or greater degree, will have the same advantages and disadvantages as the S.I.R.

The mean deviation (from the mean or median)
Generally, this is a good measure of dispersion since *all* the values are used in its computation, however, it has the disadvantage of not being soundly based mathematically (see p. 93).

The standard deviation
The S.D. has the same advantages as the mean deviation, but in addition *is* mathematically sound.

6.9 Calculation of the mean deviation from the mean of a grouped frequency distribution

Consider the grouped frequency distribution already used several times in this chapter:

Class	Frequency
$-\frac{1}{2} - +\frac{1}{2}$	1
$\frac{1}{2} - 1\frac{1}{2}$	12
$1\frac{1}{2} - 2\frac{1}{2}$	18
$2\frac{1}{2} - 3\frac{1}{2}$	24
$3\frac{1}{2} - 4\frac{1}{2}$	6
$4\frac{1}{2} - 5\frac{1}{2}$	3

First, in the manner already explained, we must calculate the mean:

Class	Mid-class value, x	Frequency, f
$-\frac{1}{2} - +\frac{1}{2}$	0	1
$\frac{1}{2} - 1\frac{1}{2}$	1	12
$1\frac{1}{2} - 2\frac{1}{2}$	2	18
$2\frac{1}{2} - 3\frac{1}{2}$	3	24
$3\frac{1}{2} - 4\frac{1}{2}$	4	6
$4\frac{1}{2} - 5\frac{1}{2}$	5	3

Mean, $\bar{x} = \dfrac{\sum fx}{\sum f}$

$$= \frac{1 \times 0 + 12 \times 1 + 18 \times 2 + 24 \times 3 + 6 \times 4 + 3 \times 5}{1 + 12 + 18 + 24 + 6 + 3}$$

$$= \frac{159}{64}$$

$= 2.5$ (correct to one decimal place)

$\bar{x} = 2.5$

We next assign deviations to each of the six classes (mid-class value (M.C.V.) minus $\bar{x}$), ignoring all negative signs:

Class	M.C.V., x	Deviation, d	Frequency, f
$-\frac{1}{2} - +\frac{1}{2}$	0	2.5	1
$\frac{1}{2} - 1\frac{1}{2}$	1	1.5	12
$1\frac{1}{2} - 2\frac{1}{2}$	2	0.5	18
$2\frac{1}{2} - 3\frac{1}{2}$	3	0.5	24
$3\frac{1}{2} - 4\frac{1}{2}$	4	1.5	6
$4\frac{1}{2} - 5\frac{1}{2}$	5	2.5	3
			$\sum f = 64$

For any set of numbers: M.D. $= \dfrac{\sum d}{n}$

Here, however, our $\sum d$ will be made up of 1 deviation of 2.5, plus 12 deviations of 1.5, etc., and our n is clearly $1 + 12 \ldots + 3 = \sum f$, i.e., in general,

$$\text{M.D.} = \frac{\sum fd}{\sum f}.$$

Thus, here the

$$\text{M.D.} = \frac{1 \times 2.5 + 12 \times 1.5 + 18 \times 0.5 + 24 \times 0.5 + 6 \times 1.5 + 3 \times 2.5}{1 + 12 + 18 + 24 + 6 + 3}$$

$$= \tfrac{58}{64}$$

$$= 0.9 \text{ (correct to one decimal place)}$$

The mean deviation from the mean is 0.9.

It is left to the reader to calculate the mean deviation from the median of the above distribution. (For the answer see page 111.)

6.10   Calculation of the standard deviation of a grouped frequency distribution

Let us consider the following distribution:

Class	Frequency
55–60	2
60–65	11
65–70	37
70–75	54
75–80	28
80–85	9
85–90	1

As for the mean deviation, we must first compute the mean of the distribution:

Class	M.C.V., x	Frequency, f
55–60	57.5	2
60–65	62.5	11
65–70	67.5	37
70–75	72.5	54
75–80	77.5	28
80–85	82.5	9
85–90	87.5	1

$$\text{Mean, } \bar{x} = \frac{\sum fx}{\sum f}$$

so here:

$$\bar{x} = \frac{115.0 + 687.5 + 2497.5 + 3915.0 + 2170.0 + 742.5 + 87.5}{2 + 11 + 37 + 54 + 28 + 9 + 1}$$

$$= \frac{10\,215.0}{142}$$

$= 72.0$ (correct to two significant figures)

Now we can assign d values to each class, together with the corresponding d^2 values:

Class	M.C.V., x	Deviation, d	d^2	Frequency, f
55–60	57.5	− 14.5	+ 210.25	2
60–65	62.5	− 9.5	+ 90.25	11
65–70	67.5	− 4.5	+ 20.25	37
70–75	72.5	+ 0.5	+ 0.25	54
75–80	77.5	+ 5.5	+ 30.25	28
80–85	82.5	+ 10.5	+ 110.25	9
85–90	87.5	+ 15.5	+ 240.25	1
				$\sum f = 142$

N.B. $d = x - \bar{x}$.

For a set of numbers: S.D. $= \sqrt{\dfrac{\sum d^2}{n}}$.

Here, however, our $\sum d^2$ will be made up of two lots of 210.25, plus eleven lots of 90.25, etc., and our n will once again be $\sum f$ (here 142), i.e., in general,

$$\text{S.D.} = \sqrt{\frac{\sum fd^2}{\sum f}} \quad \text{or} \quad \sqrt{\frac{\sum f(x - \bar{x})^2}{\sum f}}.$$

So here:

$$\text{S.D.} = \sqrt{\frac{2 \times 210.25 + 11 \times 90.25 + 37 \times 20.25 + 54 \times 0.25 + 28 \times 30.25 + 9 \times 110.25 + 1 \times 240.25}{2 + 11 + 37 + 54 + 28 + 9 + 1}}$$

$$= \sqrt{\frac{4255.5}{142}}$$

$$= \sqrt{29.97}$$

$$= 5.5 \text{ (correct to one decimal place)}$$

The standard deviation is 5.5.

N.B.   At this stage it should be mentioned that the formulae given above for the S.D. can be written in an alternative and often more convenient form (see Appendix).

6.11   Coding

The reader will no doubt feel that working out the standard deviation from a Grouped Frequency Distribution can be a painful business, and he is right! However, the advent of the pocket electronic calculator has eased the situation considerably and has made methods such as *coding*, which were originally devised to ease the burden of calculation, much less important than they were. Nevertheless it still remains a useful method for finding the mean, the mean deviation, or the standard deviation of a frequency distribution. Let us now apply the coding technique to the frequency table given above and calculate these quantities. Later on an attempt will be made to justify the formulae used.

6.12   Coding method of calculating the mean

Basically, what we do in this method is to replace a series of quantities which are difficult to handle mathematically by a series of simple ones, i.e., we codify the original data.

Example: Find the mean of the following grouped frequency distribution:

Class	Frequency
55–60	2
60–65	11
65–70	37
70–75	54
75–80	28
80–85	9
85–90	1

First, we insert the mid-class values, x:

Class	Mid-class value, x	Frequency, f
55–60	57.5	2
60–65	62.5	11

Class	Mid-class value, x	Frequency, f
65–70	67.5	37
70–75	72.5	54
75–80	77.5	28
80–85	82.5	9
85–90	87.5	1

Secondly, we note that the class interval, c, is 5; next, we must make an intelligent guess as to what the mean, $\bar{x}$, will be, choosing one of the mid-class values as our guess. Since '70–75' is the class with the greatest frequency, we make as our guess 72.5, and we call this the *assumed mean*, a. We now 'code' all our x values, replacing them by equivalent x' values where:

$$x' = \frac{x - a}{c}$$

Thus, our first x value will be:

$$x'_1 = \frac{57.5 - 72.5}{5}$$
$$\Rightarrow x'_1 = -3, \text{ etc.}$$

Finally, therefore, we get the following:

Class	x	'coded' x ($= x'$)	f
55–60	57.5	−3	2
60–65	62.5	−2	11
65–70	67.5	−1	37
70–75	72.5	0	54
75–80	77.5	+1	28
80–85	82.5	+2	9
85–90	87.5	+3	1

Since the ordinary mean, $\bar{x} = \dfrac{\sum fx}{\sum f}$, similarly the coded mean, $\bar{x}' = \dfrac{\sum fx'}{\sum f}$.

Thus, in this example,

$$\bar{x}' = \frac{2 \times (-3) + 11 \times (-2) + 37 \times (-1) + 54 \times 0 + 28 \times 1 + 9 \times 2 + 1 \times 3}{2 + 11 + 37 + 54 + 28 + 9 + 1};$$

So the coded mean is

$$\bar{x}' = \frac{-16}{142}$$

$$= -0.1 \text{ (correct to one decimal place)}$$

Now, it can be shown that the true mean, $\bar{x}$, is related to the coded mean, $\bar{x}'$, by the formula:

$$\bar{x} = c\bar{x}' + a$$

In this example

$$\bar{x} = 5 \times (-0.1) + 72.5$$

$$= -0.5 + 72.5$$

$$\Rightarrow \bar{x} = 72.0$$

The mean is 72.0.

N.B.   This is precisely the result we obtained before but this time the calculation was much less laborious.

6.13   Coding method of calculating the standard deviation

Here, we first of all calculate a 'coded' standard deviation, s', where s' is given by the following formula:

$$s' = \sqrt{\frac{\sum f(x')^2}{\sum f} - \left(\frac{\sum f(x')}{\sum f}\right)^2}$$

where x' represents the coded x values.

Although this formula may appear to be rather complicated, in practice it is not that bad. Since we are normally asked to calculate the mean, $\bar{x}$, as well as the standard deviation, s, some of the quantities under the square-root sign will already be known, *viz.*: $\sum fx'$ and $\sum f$. Generally speaking it is probably best to calculate the mean and the standard deviation in a combined operation.

Example: Find the standard deviation of the following distribution:

Class	Frequency
55–60	2
60–65	11
65–70	37
70–75	54
75–80	28
80–85	9
85–90	1

First, inserting mid-class values, x, coded x' values and columns for fx' and $f(x')^2$ we get:

Class	x	x'	f	fx'	$f(x')^2$
55–60	57.5	-3	2	-6	18
60–65	62.5	-2	11	-22	44
65–70	67.5	-1	37	-37	37
70–75	72.5	0	54	0	0
75–80	77.5	$+1$	28	$+28$	28
80–85	82.5	$+2$	9	$+18$	36
85–90	87.5	$+3$	1	$+1$	9
			$\sum f = 142$	$\sum fx' = -16$	$\sum f(x')^2 = 172$

N.B. $c = 5$; $a = 72.5$; and $x' = (x - a)/c$.

Coded standard deviation, $= \sqrt{\dfrac{\sum f(x')^2}{\sum f} - \left(\dfrac{\sum fx'}{\sum f}\right)^2}$

so in this example,

$$s' = \sqrt{\frac{172}{142} - \left(\frac{-16}{142}\right)^2}$$

$$= \sqrt{1.20}$$

i.e. coded S.D., s', is 1.1 (correct to one decimal place).

It can be shown that the true standard deviation, s, is related to the coded standard deviation, s' by the formula:

$$s = cs' \text{ (where } c \text{ is the class-width)}$$

Therefore here: $s = 5 \times 1.1 = 5.5$

The standard deviation is 5.5.

N.B.   Once again this agrees with our earlier calculation.

6.14   Proofs of the coding formulae

The mean
We have to prove that the true mean $\bar{x} = c\bar{x}' + a$, where $c =$ the class-width, $\bar{x}' =$ the coded mean, and $a =$ the assumed mean.

Since $\bar{x}' = \dfrac{\sum fx'}{\sum f}$, we have to prove that:

$$\bar{x} = \frac{c\sum fx'}{\sum f} + a \tag{1}$$

Proof

$$x' = \frac{(x - a)}{c}$$

Therefore right-hand side of equation (1)

$$= c \frac{\sum \dfrac{f(x-a)}{c}}{\sum f} + a$$

$$= \frac{c \cdot \dfrac{1}{c} \sum f(x-a)}{\sum f} + a$$

$$= \frac{\sum f(x-a)}{\sum f} + a$$

$$= \frac{\sum fx - \sum fa}{\sum f} + a$$

$$= \frac{\sum fx}{\sum f} - \frac{a \sum f}{\sum f} + a$$

$$= \frac{\sum fx}{\sum f}$$

$$= \bar{x}$$

$$= \text{left-hand side of equation (1)}$$

i.e. right-hand side = left-hand side.
Equation (1) is thus proved.

The proof of the coding formula for the standard deviation is given in the Appendix. It is also possible to calculate the mean deviation of a frequency distribution using a coding formula, but since the squaring of quantities is not involved it is doubtful whether this is really necessary. Accordingly, it is not proposed to discuss the formula.

6.15   Calculating the mean deviation (from the mean or median) and the standard deviation of a discrete frequency distribution

If the frequency distribution is discrete, we can still use the basic formulae already mentioned in connection with grouped distributions. The best procedure is probably as follows: firstly, calculate the mean, $\bar{x}$, using the formula:

$$\bar{x} = \frac{\sum fx}{\sum f}$$

and then (if it is required) calculate the standard deviation, s, using the formula:

$$s = \sqrt{\frac{\sum fx^2}{\sum f} - \bar{x}^2}$$

Thus, using the discrete frequency distribution dealt with in Chapter 5 (section 5.4) we can proceed as follows:

x	f	x^2	fx^2
0	4	0	0
1	7	1	7
2	9	4	36
3	8	9	72
4	6	16	96
5	1	25	25
	$\sum f = 35$		$\sum fx^2 = 236$

For this particular distribution we already know that $\bar{x} \simeq 2.2$ and, in fact correct to two decimal places, $\bar{x} = 2.23$.
So here:

$$s = \sqrt{\frac{\sum fx^2}{\sum f} - \bar{x}^2}$$

$$= \sqrt{\frac{236}{35} - (2.23)^2}$$

$$= 1.33$$

The standard deviation is 1.3 (correct to one decimal place).

If we are asked for the mean deviation from the mean then we use the formula:

$$\text{M.D.} = \frac{\sum fd}{\sum f}$$

where $d = x - \bar{x}$, and any negative signs are ignored. So for this distribution we have:

$d = \lvert x - \bar{x} \rvert$	f	fd
2.23(0 − 2.23)	4	8.92
1.23(1 − 2.23)	7	8.61
0.23	9	2.07
0.77	8	6.16
1.77	6	10.62
2.77	1	2.77
	$\sum f = 35$	$\sum fd = 39.15$

So

$$\text{M.D.} = \frac{\sum fd}{\sum f}$$

$$= \frac{39.15}{35}$$

$$= 1.12$$

The mean deviation is 1.1 (correct to one decimal place).

To calculate the mean deviation from the median, we proceed precisely as above except that $\bar{x}\,(2.23)$ is now replaced by the median value which is 2 (see Chapter 5, section 5.4).
So now we have:

$d = |x - median|$	f	fd
$2(= |0 - 2|)$	4	8
$1(= |1 - 2|)$	7	7
0	9	0
1	8	8
2	6	12
3	1	3
	$\sum f = 35$	$\sum fd = 38$

$$\text{M.D. from median} = \frac{\sum fd}{\sum f}$$

$$= \frac{38}{35}$$

$$= 1.09$$

The mean deviation from the median is 1.1 (correct to one decimal place).

Finally, it should be stressed that whilst coding formulae undoubtedly help to simplify and quicken the computation of quantities such as the standard deviation they are *not* essential. The reader who prefers not to use them will be able to manage perfectly well with the basic formulae; he should be prepared, however, to take longer in working out these two quantities, unless he has access to a calculator.

Exercise 6

1. Find the mean deviation of the following set of observations.

$$5 \quad 8 \quad 11 \quad 2 \quad 4 \quad 6$$

(A.E.B.)

2. Give three measures of dispersion.

3. The standard deviation of a set of 5 numbers is 7.0 and the standard deviation of

another set of 15 numbers is 6.0. Given that the two sets of numbers have the same mean, calculate the standard deviation of the combined set of 20 numbers.

(A.E.B.)

4. What is the range of a distribution?
   A. The average class interval.
   B. The sum of the frequencies.
   C. The difference between the two extreme items.
   D. A class interval multiplied by its frequency.

5. What is the variance of the set of numbers 3, 7, 9, 13?
   A. 3.61.
   B. 8.
   C. 10.
   D. 13.

(A.E.B.)

6. For the following set of numbers find (a) the range, (b) the mean deviation, (c) the standard deviation, and (d) the variance:

   27   13   26   18   23   21   27   44   27   37   34   26   28

7. Calculate the variance for the data below in which the variable is discrete.

Value of variable	1	2	3	4
Frequency	11	0	7	2

(A.E.B.)

8. Calculate the mean deviation of

   4   7   7   7   7   10

(A.E.B.)

9. (a) Calculate the standard deviation of the numbers 10, 11, 12, 13, and 14, correct to 1 decimal place.
   (b) Write down the standard deviation of the numbers 100, 110, 120, 130, and 140.
   (c) Write down the standard deviation of the numbers 43, 47, 51, 55, and 59.

10. If the standard deviation of the numbers $x_1, x_2, \ldots, x_n$ is 10, find the standard deviation of
    (a) $3x_1, 3x_2, \ldots, 3x_n$.
    (b) $2x_1 + 1, 2x_2 + 1, \ldots, 2x_n + 1$.

(A.E.B.)

11. The marks in an examination had a mean of 30 and a standard deviation (S.D.) of 8. It was decided to adjust them in order that the adjusted S.D. should be 20. If an original mark of 42 corresponds to an adjusted mark of 78, what is the mean of the adjusted marks?

(A.E.B.)

12. The pupils of a class are given some tests in arithmetic during a school term. After nine of the tests the marks of a particular pupil are:

    6,   7,   5,   8,   6,   5,   4,   6,   9.

    (a) Find the median of these marks.
    (b) Calculate the mean deviation from the median of these marks.

(J.M.B.)

13. From the following grouped frequency distribution calculate (a) the range, (b) the semi-interquartile range, (c) the '10–90' inter-percentile range, and (d) the '30–70' inter-percentile range:

Variable	Frequency
100–110	2
110–120	6
120–130	12
130–140	30
140–150	33
150–160	10
160–170	5
170–180	2

14. For the frequency distribution of question 15, calculate (a) the mean deviation and (b) the standard deviation.

15. The floor area of houses on a particular estate was calculated correct to the nearest square metre and the results are given below.

Floor area (M^2)	Cumulative frequency
20– 39	7
40– 59	23
60– 79	65
80– 99	139
100–119	212
120–139	253
140–159	272
160–179	284
180–199	292
200–259	300

Calculate
(a) the mid-class values,
(b) the frequency of each class,
(c) the arithmetic mean of the distribution,
(d) the standard deviation of the distribution.

16. The examination marks obtained by 100 candidates are distributed as follows:

Mark	0–19	20–29	30–39	40–49	50–59	60–69	70–79	80–89
Number of candidates	8	7	14	23	26	12	6	4

Make use of an assumed mean to estimate the mean and the standard deviation. A further group of 200 candidates obtained a mean mark of 52.3 with a standard deviation of 14.5 marks. Calculate the mean and the standard deviation of the whole group of 300 candidates.

(A.E.B.)

17.   A discrete variable, x, may take the values 3 and 6. In 60 trials x takes one of these values 40 times and the other value 20 times. Calculate the mean deviation of this distribution.

(A.E.B.)

18.   Calculate the standard deviation of the distribution below.

Variable	1	2	3	4
Frequency	1	2	3	4

(A.E.B.)

19.   An electronic device is made from three components, one each of types A, B, and C. Components of each type are produced by several manufacturers, the prices being shown below.

	Type A	£3, £4, £4, £5
Component	Type B	£12, £14, £15
	Type C	£1, £1, £1, £2

Draw up a frequency table of the cost of the 48 possible ways of purchasing the necessary components. Use this table to obtain for this distribution
(a) the mean,
(b) the mean deviation from the mean,
(c) the standard deviation.

(A.E.B.)

20.   The following table gives the numbers of observed weaving defects in 100 lengths of cloth.

Number of defects	≤ 17	18	19	20	21	22	≥ 23
Frequency	0	5	43	30	17	5	0

Represent the data by a suitable diagram. Calculate the standard deviation of the number of defects.

(W.J.E.C.)

21.   Recorded below are the goals scored by 60 teams on a particular Saturday.

0	5	2	3	2	2	0	1	1	0
1	1	1	0	1	0	1	1	1	2
1	0	2	3	0	1	1	1	3	2
0	1	2	0	1	5	1	1	3	1
2	1	1	3	1	3	0	2	1	2
1	2	0	2	0	1	1	0	0	1

(a) Tabulate these scores and state the type of frequency distribution to which they approximate.
(b) Use your table in order to calculate the mean number of goals scored, the standard deviation, and the mean deviation from the mean.
(c) A further 32 teams played on the same Saturday as the first 60 teams. The mean number of goals scored by all 92 teams was 1.25. Of the further 32 teams, calculate the number scoring two goals given that the remainder scored 27 goals between them.

(A.E.B.)

22.   Find the range of the following distribution.

Number of persons in family	1	2	3	4	5	6	9
Number of families	7	12	10	6	4	1	1

(A.E.B.)

23. Calculate the variance of the following distribution.

Value of variable	4	6	8	10
Frequency	240	340	200	20

(A.E.B)

24. The table below gives the distribution of scores obtained when a die was thrown 40 times.

Score	1	2	3	4	5	6
Frequency	5	8	7	6	4	10

    If a series of fives is then thrown, how many would be required for the overall arithmetic mean to be 3.8?

(A.E.B.)

Answers to the problems in Chapter 6:
page 89 : Range = 26
page 90 : S.I.R. = 0.77
page 99 : Median of Grouped Frequency Distribution = 2.54
      Mean deviation from median = 0.9 (correct to one decimal place)

7
Correlation and regression

7.1 Correlation

Suppose we were to record the weights and heights of say twenty adults. What sort of results would we expect to get? Of course, we cannot give an exact answer. We would not be able, for example, to say that anyone having a weight in kilograms of X would have a corresponding height in centimetres of Y, *but* we would be able to say that anyone who was relatively heavy was likely to be relatively tall; whilst anyone who was relatively light was likely to be relatively short.

If we now plot on a graph each *height* value against each *weight* value we obtain what is called a *scatter diagram*. The weights will be a series of x values, so these are plotted along the horizontal axis, whilst the corresponding heights will be a series of y values, plotted along the vertical axis. Suppose that we obtained the following results:

Weight, x (kilograms)	Height, y (centimetres)
57	155
61	158
62	163
64	158
65	165
72	165
75	170
76	178
80	178
83	175
85	183
89	185

Weight, x (kilograms)	Height, y (centimetres)
92	198
95	193
98	205
98	198
100	198
103	213
104	208
106	225

N.B. $\bar{x} = 83.25$, $\bar{y} = 183.55$

From this data we get the scatter diagram shown in Figure 7.1.

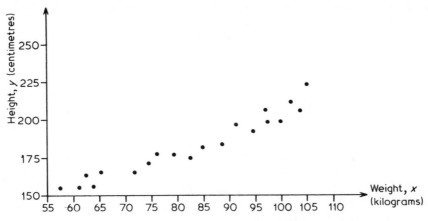

Figure 7.1 Weights and corresponding heights of twenty adults

It is quite evident that the twenty points plotted on the above diagram are not just randomly distributed, but conform to a definite pattern—here, in fact, they tend to lie along a straight line—and whenever this happens there is the possibility that some kind of relationship exists between the two variables concerned (in this case height and weight). The relationship is often a *linear* one (as here), but this is by no means always the case. If the points tend to lie along a *curve*, for example, we may have a *quadratic* relationship, and so on.

Whenever there is some connection or dependence between two or more variables, we have what is called *correlation*, i.e. we say that if a second variable y is partially or wholly dependent on a first variable x, there is some degree of correlation between them.

7.2   Patterns of correlation

Let us look at some of the more common types of scatter diagram:

1.   *No correlation*

The points are scattered in a random fashion – there is no obvious line or curve along which the points tend to lie.

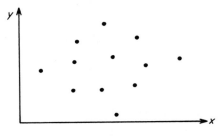

Figure 7.2

2.   *Slight positive correlation*

The points show some tendency to align themselves along a line sloping from bottom left to top right.

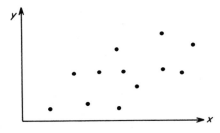

Figure 7.3

3.   *Slight negative correlation*

Similar to 2 above, but this time the line slopes from top left to bottom right.

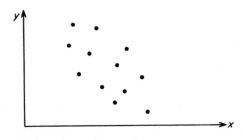

Figure 7.4

4.   *Strong positive correlation*

The points are obviously aligning themselves along a straight line of positive slope.

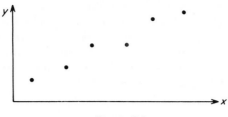

Figure 7.5

5. *Strong negative correlation*

The points are obviously aligning themselves along a straight line of negative slope.

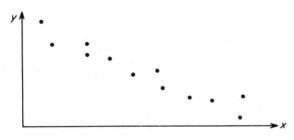

Figure 7.6

6. *Strong quadratic correlation*

Again, there is obviously a pattern, but this time the points tend to lie along a curve (a parabola in this example).

Figure 7.7

Problem: Suggest six pairs of variables which might produce the scatter diagrams illustrated in Figures 7.2–7.7. (Possible answers are given on page 131.)

7.3   Lines of regression

Let us now return to the data concerning weights and heights – and in particular the scatter diagram obtained from it. We can draw in, by eye, what is called a '*line of best fit*', and this will be useful because it will enable us to make some sensible predictions. This line is termed the *regression line of height on weight* or more generally the *regression line of y on x* and it must pass through the point $(\bar{x}, \bar{y})$, so we plot the latter *before* drawing the line.

Now, suppose we know that some-one weighs 70 kilograms, then from our graph we can predict that their height is likely to be in the region of 168 cm (see Figure 7.8).

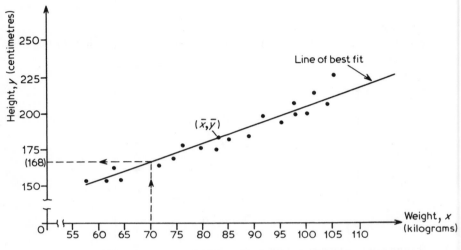

Figure 7.8 Regression line of height, y, on weight, x

We would obtain the same kind of scatter diagram if we were to plot say the 'marks in German' against the 'marks in French' for a number of examination candidates, and again we could make good *practical* use of it, for, if a candidate were present for the French exam, but missed the German exam due to illness, we could use the 'line of best fit' to estimate or predict his German mark.

7.4   Calculating the equation of a regression line

The equation of any straight line can generally be represented in the form $y = mx + c$, where m is the *gradient* (or *slope*) of the line and c is the *intercept* on the y-axis. Both m and c can be $+$ or $-$, as shown in Figure 7.9.

Let us now calculate the *equation* of the regression line of y on x, for the data concerning weights and heights. Notice that the axes of this graph do not start from the origin, and therefore we cannot estimate the intercept, c, directly from the graph. We can however, always calculate the slope, m, so let us do this first. From (Figure 7.9) the reader will see that we need to draw in two *convenient* lines running parallel to the x- and y-axes. Further, since the slope $= \pm \dfrac{Y}{X}$,

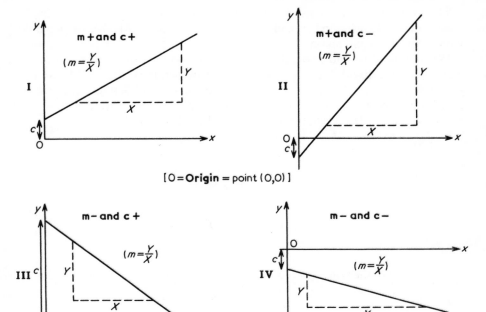

Figure 7.9

we arrange for X to be an easy numerical quantity, since this greatly simplifies the required calculation:

In Figure 7.10, we make X equal to 50 (110 − 60), for obvious reasons, and Y is found equal to 62.5 (218.8 − 156.3). Therefore the slope, $m = +\dfrac{Y}{X} = \dfrac{62.5}{50} = 1.25$;

i.e. $m = +1.25$.

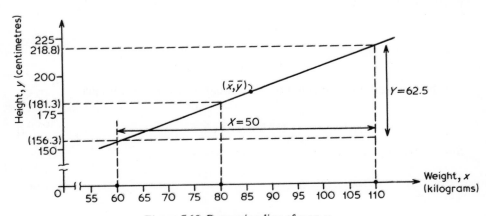

Figure 7.10 Regression line of *y* on *x*

The slope of this line is also known as the *regression coefficient*.

We could, of course, have made X equal to 25 (say) in which case Y would have been 31.25, and so on.

We now need to find c, which we cannot always measure directly from the graph since we do not have complete axes. However, from Figure 7.10 we can see that when $x = 80.0$, $y = 181.3$, and we know that all sets of (x, y) values must satisfy the equation $y = mx + c$. Accordingly, if we substitute $m = +1.25$, $x = 80.0$, and $y = 181.3$ into the latter we shall be able to find c:

$$y = mx + c,$$

therefore

$$181.3 = 1.25 \times 80 + c$$

or

$$181.3 = 100 + c$$

$$c = +81.3$$

The equation of the regression line of y on x is therefore

$$y = 1.25x + 81.3$$

N.B.   Since $(\bar{x}, \bar{y})$ lies on the line, we could have taken 83.25 and 183.55 as our values of x and y respectively.

We can, if we wish, use symbols that are more appropriate to the particular data we are dealing with. In this case, if we let h represent height and w represent weight, the equation of our regression line becomes:

$$h = 1.25w + 81.3$$

There is an alternative procedure to that mentioned above: instead of measuring m, and using one known (x, y) pair, we can use *two* (x, y) pairs and calculate both m and c from the resulting simultaneous equations.

For example, we have from the graph:

$$x = 60 \text{ when } y = 156.3$$

and

$$x = 110 \text{ when } y = 218.8$$

Substituting these results in the basic equation $y = mx + c$ we get:

$$156.3 = 60m + c \tag{1}$$

$$218.8 = 110m + c \tag{2}$$

Subtracting equation (2) from equation (1) gives us

$$-62.5 = -50m$$

Therefore

$$m = 1.25$$

Substituting $m = 1.25$ into equation (1):

$$156.3 = 60 \times 1.25 + c$$

$$\Rightarrow c = 156.3 - 75$$

i.e. $\qquad\qquad\qquad\qquad c = 81.3$

The equation of the regression line of y on x is $y = 1.25\, x + 81.3$.

One other option is available to us, provided both the x- and y-axes start from zero, i.e. the origin is present. In this case m can be calculated in the usual way and c can be measured directly from the graph.

7.5   Confirming a relationship between two variables

Before going on to deal with correlation in more detail, mention should be made of a useful method of ascertaining the relationship between two variables, *when this relationship is non-linear.* We have already said that $y = mx + c$ gives a straight-line graph of slope m and intercept c, which is obtained by plotting y against x. Similarly, for the equation $f(y) = af(x) + b$, where $f(x)$ and $f(y)$ are functions of x and y respectively, e.g. x^2, $1/x$, y^3, log y, etc., and a and b are *constants*, if we plot $f(y)$ against $f(x)$, we will *still* obtain a straight line, this time of slope a and intercept b. We can then estimate these in the usual manner, giving us the exact relationship between x and y.

Example: The following values for two variables, x and y, were obtained:

x	0.125	0.250	0.500	1.000	2.000
y	3.9	2.1	0.95	0.6	0.3

It is thought that x and y are connected by an equation of the form $y = \dfrac{a}{x} + b$.

Confirm that this is so, and find the values of a and b.

We have $y = a \times \left(\dfrac{1}{x}\right) + b$, so if this equation is correct, a graph of y against $\left(\dfrac{1}{x}\right)$ should yield a straight line of slope a and intercept b. From the above data we get:

y	3.9	2.1	0.95	0.6	0.3
$1/x$	8.0	4.0	2.0	1.0	0.5

A graph of y against $1/x$ is shown in Figure 7.11 on page 120.

Since we get a good straight line, the above equation is correct. From the graph we see that slope $= 4/8 = 0.5$, and intercept $= 0$; i.e. $a = 0.5$ and $b = 0$. The complete equation connecting x and y is therefore:

$$y = \frac{0.5}{x} + 0$$

i.e.

$$y = \frac{1}{2x}$$

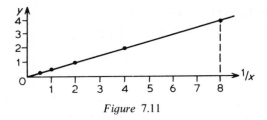

Figure 7.11

7.6   Coefficient of correlation

Apart from plotting scatter diagrams, calculating the equations of regression lines, etc., it is often useful to have *an actual measure* of the amount of correlation that exists between two given variables such as weight and height, turnover and profit, age and salary – this measure of correlation is called a *coefficient of correlation* and is normally given the symbol r. Although the formula for its precise calculation need not concern us yet, what is important is that it can only lie between -1 and $+1$, and can have no other values. Further, if the correlation coefficient, r, is numerically close to ± 1 there is good correlation; if it is numerically close to 0 there is poor correlation. For example,

$$\left. \begin{array}{l} r = +0.92 \\ r = -0.96 \end{array} \right\} \textit{good} \text{ correlation}$$

$$\left. \begin{array}{l} r = -0.12 \\ r = 0 \\ r = +0.26 \end{array} \right\} \textit{poor} \text{ or } \textit{non-existent} \text{ correlation}$$

If the correlation between two variables is such that an increase in one is accompanied by an increase in the other, the correlation is said to be *positive*: in this case the 'line of best fit' on the corresponding scatter diagram will slope from bottom left to top right. If, however, the correlation is such that an increase in one variable is accompanied by a *decrease* in the other, the correlation is said to be *negative*: in this case, of course, the 'line of best fit' will slope from top left to bottom right. These points are illustrated diagrammatically in Figures 7.12–7.14.

1.   *High positive correlation*

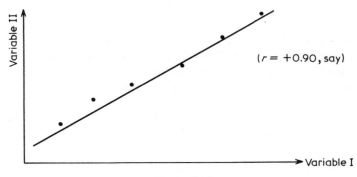

Figure 7.12

2. *High negative correlation*

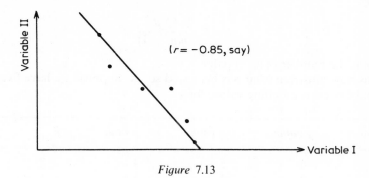

Figure 7.13

3. *Poor correlation*

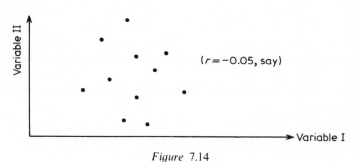

Figure 7.14

N.B.   In Figure 7.14 there is no obvious 'line of best fit'.

Although the exact calculating of *r* will be dealt with at the end of the chapter, there are several formulae available that give reasonable approximations to *r*; one of these is Spearman's formula for a *coefficient of rank correlation,* which is discussed in the next section.

7.7   Spearman's coefficient of correlation by ranks

The basic idea behind this coefficient is, as its name implies, the *ranking* of the variables, i.e. we look at our original data and only take into account the *relative* magnitude of each quantity (as opposed to the absolute magnitude). We then assign appropriate *ranks* to each set of data, the highest value being placed first and given a rank of 1, the second highest value being placed second and given a rank of 2, and so on. It is also perfectly permissible to rank both variables in the opposite manner – in which case the *lowest* value is given rank 1, the second lowest rank 2, etc.

When we have ranked both sets of variables, we work out a set of deviations or *d* values by subtracting each *y* rank from the corresponding *x* rank (or *vice versa*). Finally, we compile a set of (deviation)^2 or d^2 values, and obtain the consequent value for $\sum d^2$.

Having obtained the value of $\sum d^2$ we then use Spearman's formula for r given by

$$r = 1 - \frac{6\sum d^2}{n(n^2 - 1)}$$

where n is the number of (x, y) pairs.

Let us now illustrate what has been said so far. Suppose we have five values for x and five corresponding values for y:

x value	y value	x rank	y rank	d	d²
1	6	5	3	+2	+4
2	2	4	5	−1	+1
3	4	3	4	−1	+1
5	10	2	1	+1	+1
9	8	1	2	−1	+1
					$\sum d^2 = 8$

So, we have $\sum d^2 = 8$ and $n = 5$, then substituting in Spearman's formula, $r = 1 - \dfrac{6\sum d^2}{n(n^2 - 1)}$, we have

$$r = 1 - \frac{6 \times 8}{5(5^2 - 1)}$$

$$\Rightarrow r = 1 - \frac{48}{5 \times 24}$$

$$\Rightarrow r = 1 - \tfrac{2}{5}$$

$$r = +\tfrac{3}{5} \text{ or } +0.6.$$

i.e.   The coefficient of rank correlation is $+0.6$.

Note that we obtain a value for r that does lie within the permitted range of -1 to $+1$. The size of the coefficient implies that there is no more than fair correlation between the variables in this case.

Of course the above process is not always so simple! Thus the question arises as to what we do in the case where a variable has two or more equal values. What ranks do we assign in this case? We obviously need some kind of convention and the one generally adopted is as follows.

The rank given to each identical value is equal to the arithmetic mean of the ranks that would have been given, had all the values been different.

This sounds complicated but in practice is not. For example, suppose we had the following set of values for a variable:

2,   7,   2,   1,   2.

Treating each of the 2s as different, i.e. $2_A, 2_B$, and 2_C, we would get:

Value	Rank
7	1
2_A	2
2_B	3
2_C	4
1	5

But in reality, of course, the 2s are *not* different and so, from what has been said previously, we give each 2 a rank equal to the mean of 2, 3, and 4; $(2 + 3 + 4)/3 = 3$, so each 2 receives a rank of 3, i.e. we get:

Value	Rank
7	1
2	3
2	3
2	3
1	5

A common situation where we can use Spearman's rank correlation coefficient occurs in the realm of competitions, such as Baby Competitions or Beauty Competitions, where the variable concerned cannot readily be given a *numerical* value. Such variables are called *qualitative variables* or *attributes* and include things such as beauty or attractiveness (other examples are taste and colour).

Order of Preference	Judge I	Judge II	Judge III
1	D	D	D
2	E	H	G
3	C	G	C
4	H	A	E
5	G	E	A
6	A	C	B
7	I	B	F
8	B	I	I
9	J	F	H
10	F	J	J

The normal procedure in competitions of this kind is for a number of judges to place the contestants in order from first to last. By calculating r an appropriate number of times we can get a very good idea of just how much agreement there is between the individual judges. For example, suppose there are ten babies entered in a Baby Competition (A, B, C, D, E, F, G, H, I, and J), and suppose there are three judges (I, II, and III). The judges place the babies, in order of preference, as shown in the preceding table.

We can re-arrange this data into a more manageable form as follows:

Baby	Placed by Judge I	Placed by Judge II	Placed by Judge III
A	6	4	5
B	8	7	6
C	3	6	3
D	1	1	1
E	2	5	4
F	10	9	7
G	5	3	2
H	4	2	9
I	7	8	8
J	9	10	10

We can now work out, for example, the amount of agreement between Judges I and III by evaluating $r_{I,III}$. Then we have:

Judge I	Judge III	d	d^2
6	5	1	1
8	6	2	4
3	3	0	0
1	1	0	0
2	4	−2	4
10	7	3	9
5	2	3	9
4	9	−5	25
7	8	−1	1
9	10	−1	1
			$\sum d^2 = 54$

So here, $n = 10$ and $\sum d^2 = 54$ and substituting these values in Spearman's formula, $r = 1 - \dfrac{6\sum d^2}{n(n^2 - 1)}$, we have

$$r_{I,III} = 1 - \frac{6 \times 54}{10(10^2 - 1)}$$

$$= 1 - \frac{324}{10 \times 99}$$

$$= 1.0000 - 0.3273$$

$$= 0.6727$$

i.e.

$$\underline{r_{I,III} = 0.67 \text{ (correct to two decimal places).}}$$

This value of r suggests that there is only fair agreement between these two judges – a situation by no means uncommon in reality!

It is left to the reader, as an exercise, to calculate $r_{I,II}$ and $r_{II,III}$, and to comment on his/her results. (For the answers see page 131.)

7.8   The product-moment correlation coefficient

So far we have only worked out correlation coefficients by a ranking method where, as we have mentioned already, we take into account the *relative* sizes of the variables rather than their *absolute* sizes, and by its very nature this method can only give us approximate results.

If we *do* wish to consider the absolute values in order to obtain a more accurate result, we calculate what is called the *product-moment linear correlation coefficient*, r, which, for a set of $n(x, y)$ values is given by:

$$r = \frac{\sum(x - \bar{x}).(y - \bar{y})}{\sqrt{\sum(x - \bar{x})^2 . \sum(y - \bar{y})^2}} \tag{1}$$

There is another way of writing formula (1), which is generally easier and quicker to use when performing actual calculations, this is:

$$r = \frac{\sum xy - \dfrac{\sum x \sum y}{n}}{\sqrt{\left\{ \left[\sum x^2 - \dfrac{(\sum x)^2}{n} \right] \left[\sum y^2 - \dfrac{(\sum y)^2}{n} \right] \right\}}} \tag{2}$$

(For a proof of the equivalence of these formulae, see the Appendix.)

Let us now apply the appropriate formula to an actual problem.

Example: The weights, x, and heights, y, of twenty adults were recorded as follows:

Weight, x	Height, y	Weight, x	Height, y
57	155	85	183
61	158	89	185
62	163	92	198
64	158	95	193

Weight, x	Height, y	Weight, x	Height, y
65	165	98	205
72	165	98	198
75	170	100	198
76	178	103	213
80	178	104	208
83	175	106	225

Calculate the product-moment linear correlation coefficient for this data.
We have

$$\sum x = 57 + 61 + 62 + \ldots + 106 = 1665$$
$$\sum y = 155 + 158 + 163 + \ldots + 225 = 3671$$
$$\sum x^2 = 57^2 + 61^2 + 62^2 + \ldots + 106^2 = 143\,513$$
$$\sum y^2 = 155^2 + 158^2 + 163^2 + \ldots + 225^2 = 681\,723$$
$$\sum xy = 57 \times 155 + 61 \times 158 + 62 \times 163 \ldots + 106 \times 225 = 311\,625$$
$$n = 20$$

and
Substituting in

$$r = \frac{\sum xy - \dfrac{\sum x \cdot \sum y}{n}}{\sqrt{\left[\sum x^2 - \dfrac{(\sum x)^2}{n}\right]\left[\sum y^2 - \dfrac{(\sum y)^2}{n}\right]}}$$

we have

$$r = \frac{311\,625 - \dfrac{1665 \times 3671}{20}}{\sqrt{\left[143\,513 - \dfrac{1665^2}{20}\right]\left[681\,723 - \dfrac{3671^2}{20}\right]}}$$

$$\Rightarrow r = \frac{6014.25}{\sqrt{4901.75 \times 7910.95}}$$

$$\Rightarrow r = +0.966 \text{ (correct to two (decimal places))}$$

The product-moment linear correlation coefficient is $+0.97$.

Note that this value agrees well with Spearman's rank correlation coefficient calculated for the same data. Nevertheless, it should be emphasized that the degree of agreement between the two methods will not always be so good.

Finally, a couple of points that should be stressed. Firstly, if we have two variables that are related to each other in a *non-linear* manner, the ordinary correlation coefficient r can be positively misleading. For example, consider the scatter diagram shown in Figure 7.15.

Figure 7.15

There is obviously a strong circular relationship between the variables in Figure 7.15 but $r = 0$! Secondly, we must beware of traps. That is to say we must be very careful not to start assigning relationships that do not in fact exist. For example, there is undoubtedly a causal relationship between say latitude and temperature, i.e. an increase in latitude does normally *cause* a decrease in temperature. There is *not*, however, a causal relationship between the annual yield of sugarbeet and the number of camping holidays per year, although superficially there might appear to be a strong negative correlation between them! In fact *both* these variables depend, not on each other, but on a third variable: namely the annual rainfall.

The case of smoking and lung cancer is a further illustration. Although it had long been suspected that there was an association between the number of cigarettes smoked and the incidence of lung cancer, it took many years of painstaking research in the laboratory and elsewhere, before this association was established beyond all reasonable doubt.

Exercise 7

1. The following table shows the examination marks in French and in German of 10 students:

Student	I	II	III	IV	V	VI	VII	VIII	IX	X
French mark	21	29	39	44	55	64	68	79	86	94
German mark	33	37	43	39	51	51	53	46	59	58

(a) Plot these results on a graph and draw the line of best fit. Determine an equation relating French and German marks and use it to estimate the German mark corresponding to a French mark of 50.

(b) Calculate a coefficient of rank correlation between the French and German marks.

2. Copy Figure 7.16 and insert points which will indicate that a large negative linear correlation exists between the two variables x and y.

(A.E.B.)

Figure 7.16

3. The table below shows the marks awarded to six divers by two judges. Calculate the value of a coefficient of rank correlation.

Diver	A	B	C	D	E	F
1st judge	6.5	7.0	7.0	8.0	8.5	9.0
2nd judge	7.5	9.0	8.0	6.5	8.5	8.5

(A.E.B.)

4. (a) Three boys, X, Y, and Z, were asked to estimate by hand the weights of six objects and arrange them in descending order. The weights, in newtons, were A, 35; B, 32; C, 30; D, 30; E, 28; and F, 26. The order in which they were placed by each boy is shown below:

	A	B	C	D	E	F
X	1	3	2	4	6	5
Y	1	2	5	4	6	3
Z	2	1	4	3	6	5

Calculate coefficients of rank correlation in order to decide (i) which boy is the best judge, (ii) which two boys are most in agreement.

Comment briefly on any interesting features of your results.

(b) Twenty pairs of observations of two variables, x and y, were obtained experimentally and, after plotting a scatter diagram, a line of regression of y upon x was fitted. The whole procedure was repeated for a different pair of variables.

In each case the magnitude of the correlation coefficient was found to be 0.9 but in the first experiment the regression coefficient was 1.0 while in the second it was -0.5.

Illustrate, by means of scatter diagrams, the types of distribution encountered in these experiments.

(A.E.B.)

5.

Competitor	A	B	C	D	E	F
1st judge	1	2	3	4	5	6
2nd judge	2	3	1	5	4	6

The table gives the respective rankings of two judges for six competitors. Calculate the coefficient of rank correlation.

(A.E.B.)

6. The magnitudes of the items in a distribution are

$$10 \quad 11 \quad 18 \quad 15 \quad 7 \quad 15 \quad 16 \quad 8.$$

What is the rank of the two items of magnitude 15 if the items are arranged in descending order of magnitude?
A. 3.
B. $3\frac{1}{2}$.
C. 4.
D. $5\frac{1}{2}$.

(A.E.B.)

7. Which of the following coefficients expresses the least correlation?
A. -1.0.
B. -0.5.
C. 0.
D. 0.25.

(A.E.B.)

8. A set of pupils sat a mock 'O' Level examination in English in February and the official
    examination in July. The marks obtained by the candidates in both examinations
    were as follows:

Mock marks, M	10	15	23	31	42	43	46	61	70	72	75	76
Official marks, O	12	15	20	28	40	41	50	62	65	70	75	73

    Draw a line of regression of O on M.
      A pupil obtained 44 marks in the mock examination and was absent from the
    official examination. What would have been his probable mark for the official
    examination?
      Find a suitable equation giving O in terms of M.

9. Two competition judges, A and B, rank four ice-skaters in order of merit. Given that
    $\sum d^2 = 10$, where d denotes the difference in rank,
    (a) calculate the value of the rank correlation coefficient,
    (b) complete the set of ranks for Judge B.

Judge	Ranks
A	1 2 3 4
B	3

                                                                        (A.E.B.)

10. What does a regression coefficient measure?

                                                                        (A.E.B.)

11. The following table shows experimental values of two variables x and y.

x	5	9	13	31	48
y	5.2	6.7	7.8	10.4	12.1

    It is expected that the relationship between y and x is of the form $y = a\sqrt{x} + b$,
    where a and b are constants.

      Plot y against $\sqrt{x}$ and draw the line of best fit. Hence estimate the values of a and b.
    Use the relationship to predict a value of y when $x = 81$.

                                                                        (A.E.B.)

12. Observations of two variables x and y are plotted as points on a scatter diagram.
    A line of best fit is drawn which may be used to estimate values of y for given values
    of x. What is the term given to the gradient of this line?

                                                                        (A.E.B.)

13. Two variables have a positive linear correlation. Between what values must the
    coefficient of correlation lie?

                                                                        (A.E.B.)

14. (a) Which of the following coefficients express (i) perfect correlation, (ii) no cor-
    relation?

            $- 1.00$, $- 0.50$, 0.00, 0.50, 1.00.

    (b) A group of pupils sat a trial examination in May and the official examination
    in June. The marks obtained by the pupils in both examinations were as follows:

Trial marks	10	14	23	36	36	44	45	55	56	60	72	85
Official marks	18	7	28	40	42	45	45	45	55	50	73	68

Rank the pupils in both examinations and calculate Spearman's rank correlation coefficient.

(A.E.B.)

15. In an experiment the following values were obtained for two variables x and y.

x	0	0.5	1	1.5	2	2.5	3	3.5
y	0.6	0.45	0.8	0.85	1.4	1.65	2.4	2.85

Change to a new pair of variables X and Y, where $X = x^2$ and $Y = y$.
Plot a scatter diagram for Y against X and hence draw the line of regression for Y on X.
Find an equation for y in terms of x.

16. In a beauty contest, with three judges, A, B, and C, the correlation between the judges was as follows:

$$r_{A,B} = 0.80$$
$$r_{A,C} = 0.50$$
$$r_{B,C} = 0.60$$

(a) Given that all three judges are equally experienced, which judge would you replace and why?
(b) Would you act differently if judge C was by far the most experienced?

17. An experiment into the correlation between the two variables x and y produced the following data:

x	13.0	16.0	19.0	22.0	25.0	28.0
y	36.5	37.8	40.2	39.3	41.7	43.0

(a) Calculate Spearman's coefficient of rank correlation between x and y.
(b) Plot a scatter diagram of the data.
(c) Calculate the arithmetic mean values of x and y and use them to draw the line of best fit by eye.
(d) Obtain the equation of this line in the form $y = Ax + B$ where A and B are given correct to two significant figures.
(e) Assuming extrapolation to be valid, use your equation to calculate the most probable value of y when $x = 10$.

(A.E.B.)

18. Explain what is meant by the terms *positive* and *negative* correlation, illustrating your answer by means of suitable diagrams.
What is the value of the product moment correlation coefficient if two variables are (a) perfectly correlated, (b) uncorrelated?
The selling prices of six second-hand bicylces in relation to their ages were noted for advertisements appearing in a local newspaper. The details are given in the table below.

Age, x (years)	4	10	2	1	3	4
Price, y	9	1	14	18	12	7

Draw a scatter diagram to illustrate the data.
Calculate the value of the product-moment correlation coefficient and state what you infer from its value.

The product-moment correlation coefficient may be calculated from the formula:

$$r = \frac{n(\sum xy) - (\sum x)(\sum y)}{\sqrt{\{n(\sum x^2) - (\sum x)^2\}} \sqrt{\{n(\sum y^2) - (\sum y)^2\}}}$$

(W.J.E.C.)

19. Each of five essays was awarded marks out of a possible maximum of 10 by two independent judges. The marks awarded are shown below.

Essay	P	Q	R	S	T
Judge A	8	6	10	3	4
Judge B	9	5	7	4	8

Calculate a coefficient of rank correlation.

(A.E.B.)

20. An investigation into the correlation between two variables x and y produced the following data:

x	12.0	19.6	28.0	16.0	24.0	20.4
y	21.0	33.5	45.0	27.0	39.0	32.5

(a) Calculate Spearman's coefficient for the rank correlation between x and y.
(b) Plot a scatter diagram of the data.
(c) Calculate the arithmetic mean values of x and y and use them to draw a line of best fit.
(d) Obtain the equation of this line in the form $y = Ax + B$ where A and B are given correct to two significant figures.
(e) Write down the corresponding value given by your graph.

(A.E.B.)

21. From a group of observations of a pair of variables, x and y, it is found that the regression coefficient of y on x is -0.5. The line of regression of y on x passes through the point $(1, 8)$. Estimate the value of y when $x = 7$.

(A.E.B.)

Answers to the problems in Chapter 7:
page 115: Figure 7.2   Height and annual salary
          Figure 7.3   Age and annual salary
          Figure 7.4   Latitude and average temperature
          Figure 7.5   Depth below ground and temperature
          Figure 7.6   Miles per gallon and engine size
          Figure 7.7   Average speed and miles per gallon
page 125: $r_{I,II} = 0.79$; $r_{II,III} = 0.60$.

8
Time series

8.1 Time series

Time series were briefly mentioned earlier (see page 45) and the purpose here is to consider them in more detail.

If we keep records of some quantity such as profits, football attendances, unemployment figures, etc., in fact anything that varies with time, then, by plotting the particular variable concerned (along the vertical axis) against time (along the horizontal axis), we obtain what is known as a *time series*. Let us consider a hypothetical example. Figure 8.1 shows the sales of ice-cream, quarter by quarter, over a five-year period for the company Nice-Ice Ltd:

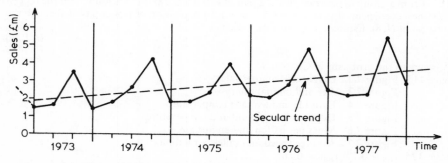

Figure 8.1 Five complete cycles of the seasonal variation in the sales of ice cream

Now most time series, including the one just illustrated, exhibit a number of different elements and two of the most important are discussed in sections 8.2 and 8.3.

8.2 Secular trend

The *secular trend* is simply the general or overall trend of the data, i.e. it shows whether the data is tending to increase or decrease with time (or whether it is doing neither). In the above time series, the secular trend has been drawn in with a broken line, and in this particular case it can be seen that ice-cream sales are gradually increasing.

8.3   Seasonal variation

Many industries do not experience an even demand for their products throughout the year. For example, car sales tend to be highest in the spring and pre-summer period, since many people like to have a new car before going on holiday. Since the practice of changing the registration plate letter on 1st August was established, there has been a tendency for people to delay purchase until this date. Similarly, toy sales show a sharp rise in December due to the imminence of Christmas. These fluctuations, due to seasonal factors, are known as *seasonal variations*, and if we look at the time series illustrated in Figure 8.1, variations are clearly present. As we would expect, ice-cream sales are seen to be fairly stagnant for the January-March quarter, show some tendency to increase for the April-June quarter, and are particularly buoyant in the July-September quarter when (a) the weather tends to be at its hottest and (b) most people take their summer holiday. Predictably, sales decline sharply during the October-December quarter. Note that the seasonal-variation pattern roughly repeats itself from year to year, i.e. it recurs in cycles (see Figure 8.1).

8.4   Other elements

There are other elements that may be present in a time series, including *cyclical fluctuations*. These are fluctuations that repeat themselves every three or four years say, i.e. they are essentially long-term as opposed to the short-term nature of seasonal variations. *Irregular fluctuations* may also be present, and in this case some agency or other will generally be responsible. For example, if there were a prolonged strike at Nice-Ice Ltd in the spring, this would clearly bring down the sales for the July-September quarter.

It is perhaps instructive to try and illustrate a further hypothetical time series which contains *all* the above elements, so that we can distinguish clearly between them. Accordingly, this is represented in Figure 8.2.

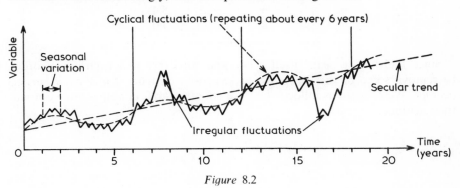

Figure 8.2

The difficulty with many time series is in deciding just where the secular trend line should be drawn. This is an important matter, e.g. in the case of the chart for ice-cream sales, once we have drawn in the trend line we can make some kind of prediction of what sales are likely to be in 1978 and 1979. Obviously, it is extremely useful to any company to know, *in advance*, just how many employees and how much machinery it is likely to need in the future. What we often need is some method of 'smoothing out' the original data, so that the overall trend becomes easier to see. Such a method has been devised and is known as the method of *moving averages.*

8.5   Moving averages

The time series on ice-cream sales was based on the following imaginary data:

Year	Quarter	Sales (£m)
1973	1	1.4
	2	1.8
	3	3.5
	4	1.3
1974	1	1.8
	2	2.7
	3	4.2
	4	1.9
1975	1	1.9
	2	2.4
	3	4.0
	4	2.2
1976	1	2.1
	2	2.9
	3	4.8
	4	2.6
1977	1	2.3
	2	2.4
	3	5.4
	4	3.0

Since the data 'repeats' itself every year (or every *four* quarters in order to remove some of the 'jerkiness' present, we construct a *four-point moving average.* We proceed as follows: first, we take the top four values and compute their arithmetic mean:

$$\left.\begin{array}{c}1.4\\1.8\\3.5\\1.3\end{array}\right\} - - - \to 2.0$$

Then we take the next possible set of four values and repeat the process.

$$
\left.\begin{array}{l}
1.4 \\
1.8 \\
3.5 \\
1.3 \\
1.8
\end{array}\right\} - - - \to 2.1
$$

We now continue until all possible sets of four have been covered.

N.B.   Two points: (1) we obtain fewer values than in the original data (17 as opposed to 20) (2) our 'moving-averages' will have to be plotted half way between quarters, since half way along any four values always brings us to a point mid-way between the second and third value.

Accordingly, we obtain the following results:

Original data	Four-point moving average
1.4	—
1.8	2.00
3.5	2.10
1.3	2.33
1.8	2.50
2.7	2.65
4.2	2.68
1.9	2.60
1.9	2.55
2.4	2.63
4.0	2.68
2.2	2.80
2.1	3.00
2.9	3.10
4.8	3.15
2.6	3.03
2.3	3.18
2.4	3.28
5.4	—
3.0	

If we now plot these 'moving-averages' against time, we obtain a series of points through which it is much easier to draw a line of best fit, as shown in Figure 8.3 on page 136.

Let us now use Figure 8.3 to predict sales of ice-cream for the first quarter of 1978.

We do this by initially reading off the next moving average: in this case about 3.35. Now, let the sales for the first quarter of 1978 be x, then from our original data:

$$\frac{2.4 + 5.4 + 3.0 + x}{4} = 3.35$$

i.e.

$$2.4 + 5.4 + 3.0 + x = 13.4$$

or

$$10.8 + x = 13.4$$

giving

$$x = 2.6$$

Thus, we can predict that sales of ice-cream in the first quarter of 1978 will be £2.6m. For the sake of simplicity no allowance has been made for inflation.

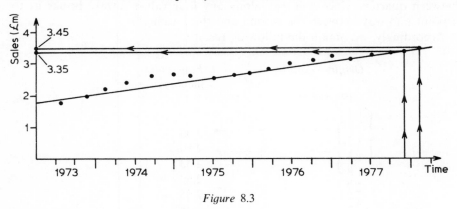

Figure 8.3

We can now, if we wish, similarly predict sales for the *second* quarter. Thus, if we read off the next moving average from our graph we get a value of about 3.45. So, if we let the sales be y, we know that:

$$\frac{5.4 + 3.0 + 2.6 + y}{4} = 3.45$$

This gives a value for y of 2.8, and so on.

A very important point always is to decide whether a three-, four-, five- or six-point moving average is required, and this depends on the nature of the original data. For example, if it repeats itself every third value, we would use a three-point moving average; if it repeats itself in cycles of six, a six-point moving average would be suitable, and so on. Generally, the pattern of repetition (if it exists) is a fairly obvious one once a time series on the original data has been plotted.

A further point about three- or five-point moving averages is that these are plotted *directly opposite* the original data, and not half way between values as for four-point moving averages. This is because half way along three values always brings us to the second, and half way along five to the third. Six-point moving averages on the other hand are like four-point and are plotted in an intermediate position. By way of illustration let us take seven values and work out their three-, four-, five-, and six-point moving averages:

Original data	Moving averages			
	Three-point	Four-point	Five-point	Six-point
23				
21	22.7			
		23.3		
24	23.3		23.4	
		23.5		23.8
25	24.3		24.0	
		24.8		24.2
24	25.0		24.8	
		25.0		
26	25.0			
25				

In general, of course, all 'even'-point moving averages are plotted like four- or six-point and all 'odd'-point moving averages like three- or five-point.

Exercise 8

1. State briefly the purpose of moving averages.
    The figures given below are observations of a variable taken at equal consecutive intervals of time.

    3.4, 4.0, 1.6, 5.2, 5.9, 4.5, 4.9, 5.2, 3.7, 7.5, 8.0, 6.8, 6.8, 7.0, 5.9, 9.7, 9.9, 8.5, 8.6, 8.8, 7.4, 10.8, 11.7, 10.5.

    Illustrate these figures on a graph.
    Using the most appropriate number of observations, calculate moving averages and illustrate these on the same graph. Estimate the next value of the observed variable.
    (A.E.B.)

2. (a) Explain what is meant in a time series by (i) seasonal variation, (ii) general trend.
    (b) The table below gives the monthly values of the index of industrial production from January 1961 to June 1962 for all industries. (Average 1958 = 100.) Represent this information graphically,
    Smooth the series by calculating the three-monthly moving averages and plot these moving averages on the same graph. State any deductions that can be made.

Month	Index	Month	Index
Jan.	112	Oct.	118
Feb.	117	Nov.	119
March	118	Dec.	112
April	115	Jan.	111
May	114	Feb.	117
June	118	March	120
July	110	April	113
August	96	May	119
Sept.	116	June	116

(A.E.B.)

3. Determine the value of the second average in a three point moving average for the values

    13   21   17   10   15   20   26   18   14

    (A.E.B.)

4. An industrial concern maintains a record of the number of day's work lost through illness. The records for three years are summarized below, each figure representing the number of day's work lost during a two-month period.

Year	Number of days work lost					
1975	217	242	161	118	102	159
1976	226	241	180	120	109	160
1977	232	245	214	126	105	177

    Draw a graph to illustrate these figures and on it superimpose a graph of the moving average using the most appropriate number of observations.
    Draw the straight line which indicates the general trend and use it to estimate the next two values of the moving average. Hence estimate the number of day's work lost in the second period of 1978.

    (A.E.B.)

5. Explain what is meant by seasonal variation in a time series.

    (A.E.B.)

6. The following table gives the takings (in £ 1000s) of a shopkeeper in each quarter of four successive years. Draw a graph to illustrate the data and on it superimpose a graph of the four-quarterly moving average. State the conclusions to be drawn from the graphs.

Year	1st	Quarter		
		2nd	3rd	4th
1974	13	22	58	23
1975	16	28	61	25
1976	17	29	61	26
1977	18	30	65	29

    (A.E.B.)

7. Find the value of the second average in a five-point moving average for the following series.

    21   23   24   27   28   30   35   34

    (A.E.B)

8. Distinguish between secular and seasonal variation.

    (A.E.B.)

9. The information in the following table is obtained from a report of a Medical Officer of Health of a local authority.

Year	Number of deaths from Lung cancer	Number of deaths from Tuberculosis
1967	22	71
1968	54	45
1969	52	54
1970	53	38
1971	46	36
1972	71	28
1973	90	24
1974	105	24
1975	82	18
1976	105	18
1977	112	12

Calculate the five-year moving averages for each disease and draw a trend curve or line for each of the sets of averages. From your curves estimate the number of deaths from each disease in the year 1978.

(O&C.)

10. The table below shows the figures for the number of articles sold by a manufacturing firm over the three-year period 1976–1977:

Year	Quarter 1	Quarter 2	Quarter 3	Quarter 4
1975	670	630	680	700
1976	740	700	760	780
1977	820	800	840	888

(a) Calculate the four-quarterly moving averages. Using a scale of 2 cm to represent 25 articles on the vertical axis, and allowing for values from 600, represent the above data graphically and mark clearly on your graph the four-quarterly moving averages.
(b) Draw the trend line on the graph, and use it to calculate the output for the first quarter of 1978.

(N.I.)

11. Observations of a variable are made once a month for 5 years. How many values of a twelve-point moving average would these give?

(A.E.B.)

12. The figures below are observations of a variable taken at equal consecutive intervals of time. Using the most appropriate number of observations, calculate the value of the fifth moving average.

3.7   4.1   4.5   4.2   3.9   3.6   2.8   3.2   3.6   3.3   3.0   2.7

(A.E.B.)

13. The average weekly sales in £ of two firms P and Q during the period 1971 to 1973 were as follows:

Firm	1971			1972			1973		
	Jan.–Apl.	May–Aug.	Sep.–Dec.	Jan.–Apl.	May–Aug.	Sep.–Dec.	Jan.–Apl.	May–Aug.	Sep.–Dec.
P	275	250	300	500	475	525	725	700	750
Q	500	365	410	575	440	485	650	515	560

(a) Using 2 cm to represent £100 and to represent 4 months, plot both sets of data on the same graph.

(b) For each firm, calculate an appropriate moving average to eliminate the seasonal variation in the sales.

(c) Plot the two moving averages on your graph.

(d) Use your graph to determine the period in which the moving average for firm P first equalled the moving average for firm Q.

(e) State, with reasons, which firm experienced the greater seasonal variation.

(f) Estimate the average weekly sales of firm P during the first four months of 1974.

(A.E.B.)

9
Weighted averages

9.1 Weighted averages (or means)

When we worked out, in an earlier chapter, the arithmetic mean or 'average' of a set of numbers, we merely added them together and divided by the number in the set. When, however, we worked out the average value of a Grouped Frequency Distribution, we had to make use of the formula:

$$\bar{x} = \frac{f_1 x_1 + f_2 x_2 + f_3 x_3 + \ldots + f_n x_n}{f_1 + f_2 + f_3 + \ldots + f_n}$$

or

$$\bar{x} = \frac{\sum fx}{\sum f}$$

Now this expression is in fact an example of a *weighted average*, the values f_1, f_2, f_3, etc. giving us the 'weight' or relative importance that should be attached to each of the values x_1, x_2, x_3, and so on. Of course, very often we will want to work out a weighted average from other sources, and so in general we define a weighted average as follows:

If we have values $x_1, x_2, x_3, \ldots, x_n$, each having weights of $w_1, w_2, w_3, \ldots, w_n$ respectively, then their weighted mean $\bar{x}_w$ is given by:

$$\bar{x}_w = \frac{w_1 x_1 + w_2 x_2 + w_3 x_3 + \ldots + w_n x_n}{w_1 + w_2 + w_3 + \ldots + w_n}$$

or

$$\bar{x}_w = \frac{\sum wx}{\sum w}$$

Example: Find the weighted mean of the following data:

Value, x	Weight, w
107	20
102	5
109	10

Now $\bar{x}_w = \sum wx / \sum w$, so here:

$$\bar{x}_w = \frac{20 \times 107 + 5 \times 102 + 10 \times 109}{20 + 5 + 10}$$

thus

$$\bar{x}_w = \frac{3740}{35}$$

$$\Rightarrow \bar{x}_w = 106.9 \text{ (correct to one decimal place)}$$

The weighted mean is 106.9

9.2   Index numbers

Index numbers are a very useful way of showing how some quantity, such as industrial production or the cost of living, is fluctuating with time. The basic principle on which they work is that at some arbitrary time in the past the quantity concerned is taken to have a value of 100 and all future values are worked out on this basis. Thus, suppose the Cost-of-Living Index for 1972 is taken to be 100, and the Index for 1973 turns out to be 127 say, then it can easily be seen that in one year the cost of living has increased by 27 per cent or 27 points. Just how something like a Cost-of-Living Index can be worked out is explained in the following paragraph.

9.3   Price and percentage relatives

Suppose we have the prices of a number of different commodities at two points in time, say 1972 and 1973:

Commodity	1972	1973
Meat (per lb)	37p	50p
Fish (per lb)	25p	30p
Eggs (per doz)	28p	20p

To work out their *percentage relatives* we take all the earliest prices to be 100 and work out the later prices in proportion. Let us take meat as an example: to convert 37 into 100 we must multiply it by 100/37 and we therefore multiply the later price by 100/37 also. The percentage relative for 1973 is therefore

$$50 \times \tfrac{100}{37} = 135.1$$

In practice, to obtain each percentage relative the rule is:
Divide the later price by the earlier price (which gives the *price relative*), and then multiply by 100.

If we do this for the above commodities, we obtain the following results:

Percentage relatives	1972	1973
Meat	100	135.1
Fish	100	120.0
Eggs	100	71.4

Let us now illustrate how, with the aid of percentage relatives, we can work out a Cost-of-Living Index.

Consider the following hypothetical data for the two years 1970 and 1973:

Item of expenditure	Percentage relatives 1970	1973	Average expenditure per £1
Food	100	160	35p
Housing	100	175	20p
Heating	100	125	15p
Clothing	100	130	10p
Miscellaneous	100	120	20p

We now take the Cost-of-Living Index for the earlier period of 1970 to be 100, and in order to calculate the Index for 1973 we must calculate the weighted mean of the individual percentage relatives, the weights this time being provided by the 'average expenditure' figures in the right-hand column. Accordingly, the Index for 1973 will be:

$$\frac{35 \times 160 + 20 \times 175 + 15 \times 125 + 10 \times 130 + 20 \times 120}{35 + 20 + 15 + 10 + 20}$$

$$= 146.8 \text{ (correct to one decimal place)}$$

On the basis of the above figure, therefore, we can see that in three years the cost-of-living increased by about 47 per cent.

9.4   Chain-based indexes

Indexes can be calculated in two different ways. For example, we might be told that, taking 1975 as 100, the Cost-of-Living Index for the next three years was as follows:

Year	1976	1977	1978	
Cost-of-Living Index	106	118.7	130.6	(A)

There is an alternative method of giving this information, however, using *chain-based indexes*, i.e.:

Year	1976	1977	1978	
Cost-of-Living Index	106	112	110	(B)

Now at first sight (A) and (B) appear to be completely at variance with one another, but in fact they tell the same story. Let us try and explain why.

Chain-based indexes are calculated on the premise that the index immediately preceding it is always taken to be 100, and the effect of this, even in a situation where the cost-of-living may be steadily rising, is to reduce the magnitude of later indexes considerably. Let us now show that (B) is in fact compatible with (A).

From (B) the 1977 index is 112, taking 1976 to be 100. Therefore, by simple proportion, if we take the 1976 figure to be 106, the 1977 figure will be

$$112 \times \tfrac{106}{100} = 118.7$$

Similarly, the 1978 figure is 110 taking the 1977 figure to be 100. Therefore, taking the 1977 figure to be 118.7, once again, by simple proportion, the 1978 figure will now be

$$110 \times \frac{118.7}{100} = 130.6$$

The reader will see that these are the figures present in (A).

Examples:

1. The table below gives the percentage relatives of a certain commodity for the three years 1971–1973 inclusive, calculated on the chain-base method.

Year	1971	1972	1973
Percentage relative	137.5	118.2	115.4

(a) If the commodity cost 40p in 1970, calculate its cost in each of the years 1971, 1972, and 1973.

(b) Calculate the indexes for 1972 and 1973 taking 1970 as 100.

(a) 1971: we have 40p = 100 per cent; therefore,

$$137.5 \text{ per cent} = \frac{40}{100} \times 137.5\text{p} = 55\text{p}$$

1972: we have 55p = 100 per cent; therefore,

$$118.2 \text{ per cent} = \frac{55}{100} \times 118.2\text{p} = 65\text{p}$$

1973: we have 65p = 100 per cent; therefore,

$$115.4 \text{ per cent} = \frac{65}{100} \times 115.4p = 75p$$

The costs in 1971, 1972, and 1973 are 55, 65, and 75p respectively.

(b)   1972: we have 40p = 100 per cent, so 65p represents an index number of

$$\tfrac{100}{40} \times 65 = 162.5$$

1973: again, 40p = 100 per cent, so 75p represents an index number of

$$\tfrac{100}{40} \times 74.9 = 187.5$$

The index numbers for 1972 and 1973 are 162.5 and 187.5 respectively.

---

2.   The index numbers for the volume of exports of a certain country were as follows (1970 = 100):

Year	1975	1976
Index numbers	120	145

(a)   What are the 1970 and 1975 index numbers if 1976 = 100?

(b)   What is the 1976 index number calculated on the chain-base method?

(a)   The original index for 1976 is 145, and to scale this down to 100 we must multiply by a factor of $\tfrac{100}{145}$. Therefore, we must multiply each of the other indexes by the same factor, i.e. the new index for 1970 is

$$100 \times \tfrac{100}{145} = 69.0$$

and the new index for 1975 is

$$120 \times \tfrac{100}{145} = 82.8$$

The 1970 index number is 69.0; the 1975 index number is 82.8.

(b)   The 1975 index is 120 and the 1976 index is 145. Therefore, if the 1975 index becomes 100, the 1976 index, by proportion, will become

$$100 \times \tfrac{145}{120} = 120.8.$$

On the chain-base method: the 1976 index is 120.8

9.5   Birth-rates

The *birth-rate* for a particular population is defined as the number of *live* births per thousand of that population in a given year. Thus in 1973 the birth-rate for the United Kingdom was 13.9. If we take the total population for that year to be about 56 000 000, the number of live births was $13.9 \times 56\,000 \simeq 778\,400$.

9.6   Crude death-rates

The *crude death-rate* for a particular population is defined as the number of deaths per thousand of that population in a given year. Thus, if a town having a population of 40 000 recorded 800 deaths in a certain year, the *crude death-rate* would be

$$\frac{800}{40\ 000} \times 1000 = 20.0 \text{ per thousand}$$

A knowledge of birth- and death-rates for the country as a whole is obviously useful to any government, for these indicate whether the overall population is increasing or decreasing, and at what rate. On this basis it can then make sensible plans as to the number of new houses, hospitals, schools, roads, etc., likely to be needed in the future. The reader can therefore appreciate the importance of these quantities.

9.7   Standardized death-rates

Quite often the crude death-rate can be misleading. For example, in a town having a high proportion of retired and elderly people, it will obviously be high, whereas in a New Town, where there will be a high proportion of young people, it will be low.

In practice, therefore, the usual procedure is to split up the population of each town into a number of different age-groups, calculate the death-rate for each group, and then work out a weighted mean of these, using as weights the total population of each group *in the country as a whole*. By this means we obtain the *standardized death-rate*.

Example: A certain town, having a population of 40 000, recorded the following deaths in a certain year:

Age group	Deaths	Population	Population in country (millions)
0–20	72	12 500	16
20–40	40	9 500	15
40–60	250	10 000	14
60 +	720	8 000	10

Calculate the standardized death-rate and the crude death-rate for the town.

We have: death-rate for the 0–20 age group is

$$\frac{72}{12\ 500} \times 1000 = 5.8 \text{ (correct to one decimal place)}$$

and, by precisely similar calculations the death-rates for the other groups are:

$$20\text{--}40: \ 4.2$$
$$40\text{--}60: 25.0$$
$$60 + \ \ : 90.0$$

To obtain the standardized death-rate we now work out a weighted mean of the various 'group' death-rates. This gives us

Age group	Death-rate	Weight
0–20	5.8	16
20–40	4.2	15
40–60	25.0	14
60 +	90.0	10

So the standardized death-rate (S.D.R.) is given by:

$$\text{S.D.R.} = \frac{16 \times 5.8 + 15 \times 4.2 + 14 \times 25.0 + 10 \times 90.0}{16 + 15 + 14 + 10}$$

$$= \frac{92.8 + 63.0 + 350.0 + 900.0}{55}$$

$$= \frac{1405.8}{55}$$

$$= 25.6 \text{ (correct to one decimal place)}$$

The standardized death-rate is 25.6.

To evaluate the crude death-rate we merely need to know the *total* number of deaths and the *total* population.

Total number of deaths = 72 + 40 + 250 + 720 = 1082
Total population = 40 000
Therefore, crude death-rate (C.D.R.) is

$$\frac{1082}{40\,000} \times 1000 = 27.1 \text{ (correct to one decimal place)}$$

The crude death-rate is 27.1.

The fact that the C.D.R. here is slightly greater than the S.D.R. would suggest that the proportion of elderly people in this particular town is somewhat higher than the national average.

Exercise 9

1. The mean wages of 100, 150, and 250 men employed by three different firms are £57, £69, and £54 per week respectively. Calculate the mean wage per week of all of the men.

    (A.E.B.)

2. The mean value of 20 observations is 3.5 but the mean value of 12 of these observations is 4.3. Calculate the mean value of the remaining 8 observations.

    (A.E.B.)

3. Explain briefly what is meant by a weighted mean.
    At the beginning of a school year the children of a particular class investigated the pattern of spending in their area. Each of six items was given a certain weight and an initial price relative of 100. During the school year various increases in price occurred. The weights and the percentage increases in price are shown below.

Item	Weight	Percentage increase in price
Food	350	25
Household goods	110	21
Clothing	95	12
Housing	90	8
Fuel and light	65	18
Miscellaneous	100	13

What is the value of the Cost-of-Living Index at the beginning, and at the end, of the school year?

(A.E.B.)

4. The table below shows the number of deaths occurring in a particular year in each of two towns, X and Y, together with the population of each town and of the country. All are classified by age group.

Age group (years)	Number of deaths		Population		Country (millions)
	Town X	Town Y	Town X	Town Y	
0–	21	48	3000	8000	15
20–	7	15	3500	7500	14
40–	32	77	2500	3500	13
60 and over	88	80	1000	1000	8

Calculate crude and standardized death-rates for each town.

(A.E.B.)

5. The table below gives the price relative for a commodity for the four years 1965–1968. The price relative is calculated on the chain-base method, that is the value of the item is calculated as a percentage of its value in the previous year.

Year	1965	1966	1967	1968
Price relative (chain base)	97.5	103	98	102

If the commodity cost £12.50 in 1964 calculate its value in each of the years 1965 to 1968.

(A.E.B.)

6. The 1956 and 1961 index numbers for volume of imports were 110 and 135 (1954 = 100).
    (a) What are the 1954 and 1961 index numbers if 1956 = 100?
    (b) What are the 1954 and 1956 index numbers if 1961 = 100?

(A.E.B.)

7. Explain why a standardized death-rate is usually preferred to the crude death-rate.

In the first three columns of the table below are shown the age groups, the corresponding death-rates, and the number of deaths for a particular town in a given year. The final column gives the age distribution of the population of the county in which the town is situated.

Age group (years)	Death-rate (per 1000)	Number of deaths	Population of county (100 000s)
0–4	4.3	16	3.4
5–14	0.6	5	7.7
15–24	0.8	8	6.2
25–34	1.2	13	7.2
35–44	2.8	35	5.8
45–54	7.4	90	6.7
55–64	20.7	248	6.2
65 and over	122.3	1284	4.8

Calculate
(a) the standardized death-rate for the town,
(b) the population, to the nearest 100, of the town by age groups,
(c) the crude death-rate for the town.

(A.E.B.)

8. The index number of a commodity in 1972 was 125, taking 1970 as base year. If the 1972 price was £67.50 calculate the price in 1970.

9. The prices of a commodity in 1971 and 1974 were 35p and 45p respectively. What is the price relative for the commodity in 1974 if 1971 = 100?

(A.E.B.)

10.

Commodity	A	B	C	D
Index	101	103	105	102
Weight	2	3	4	2

Calculate a suitable index for the combined commodities.

(A.E.B.)

11. The index of retail prices of an article in 1966 was 110, and in 1968 was 120. If the price of the article in 1968 was £24, what was the price in 1966?
A. £19.20.
B. £20.
C. £21.60.
D. £22.

(A.E.B.)

12.

Year	1968	1969	1970	
Index number	104	106	108	(1962 = 100)

Taking 1968 = 100, what is the index number for 1969?
A. 98.1.
B. 101.9.
C. 102.0.
D. 106.0.

(A.E.B.)

13. Calculate an index number, using the prices and weights given in the table below, for a change in the cost-of-living between 1967 and 1977.

Commodity	Price (p) 1967	1977	Weight
Milk (per pint)	6	12	$32\frac{1}{2}$
Bread (per loaf)	7	20	42
Meat (per pound)	35	60	49
Vegetables (per pound)	6	16	35

14. (a) Contrast crude and standardized death-rates.
(b) The following table gives the relevant vital statistics for a certain town for 1965.

Age group	Number of deaths	Population (thousands)	Population in United Kingdom (millions)
0 and under 15	216	8	12
15 and under 25	200	26	7
25 and under 45	288	24	14
45 and under 65	156	6	13
65 and over	105	1	6

Calculate the crude death-rate for each age group and the standardized death-rate for the town.

(A.E.B.)

15. The index numbers, calculated on the chain-base method, for a particular commodity are shown below. Calculate the 1970 index, to the nearest whole number, using 1968 as base.

1968	1969	1970
100	107	108

(A.E.B.)

16. The price of a certain commodity in each of the years 1970 to 1973 is shown below.

Year	1970	1971	1972	1973
Price	£2.00	£2.40	£3.00	£3.30

Starting with 100 for 1970 calculate index numbers for 1971, 1972, and 1973 using the chain-base method.

(A.E.B.)

17.

Commodity	A	B	C	D
Index	103	—	112	115
Weight	3	3	2	1

Given that the weighted index for the four commodities shown above is 105, find the index for commodity B.

(A.E.B.)

18. Each of three boys receives 40p per week pocket money while each of nine girls receives 50p per week pocket money. Calculate the average weekly pocket money for all twelve children.

(A.E.B.)

10
Probability

Before we can begin to study *probability*, we really need to understand the various ways in which objects can be disposed: in particular we need to know about *permutations* and *combinations*.

10.1 Permutations (sometimes called **arrangements**)

Suppose we have 3 empty spaces on a bookshelf:

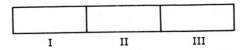

| I | II | III |

and that we have 7 different books available. In how many ways may we fill the spaces?

We can fill space I in 7 different ways. Having done this we have 6 books left with which to fill space II. Clearly this can be done in 6 different ways. Similarly, there will be 5 different ways of filling space III. Therefore the total number of different ways of filling our 3 spaces will be:

$$7 \times 6 \times 5 = 210$$

We can express the above result as:

$$\text{Number of ways} = \frac{7 \times 6 \times 5 \times 4 \times 3 \times 2 \times 1}{4 \times 3 \times 2 \times 1}$$

However, $n(n-1)(n-2)(n-3)\dots 3.2.1$ is known as *factorial n* or $n!$ so,

$$\text{Number of ways} = \frac{7!}{4!}$$

$$= \frac{7!}{(7-3)!}$$

Thus, the number of different ways of *permuting* (*arranging*) 7 objects, taken 3 at a time, is

$$\frac{7!}{(7-3)!} \text{ or } _7P_3$$

In general:

The number of different ways of permuting (arranging) n different objects, taken r at a time, is:

$$_nP_r \text{ or } \frac{n!}{(n-r)!}$$

10.2 Combinations (sometimes called **selections**)

Suppose we wish to select a doubles partnership from 5 possible tennis players; in how many ways can this be done? (Note that here we are not at all concerned with the order of the 2 players, once they have been selected).

If we call the players P_1, P_2, P_3, P_4, and P_5, then the following 10 pairs are possible:

$$
\begin{array}{ll}
P_1 P_2 & P_2 P_4 \\
P_1 P_3 & P_2 P_5 \\
P_1 P_4 & P_3 P_4 \\
P_1 P_5 & P_3 P_5 \\
P_2 P_3 & P_4 P_5
\end{array}
$$

N.B. $P_5 P_3$ is not different from $P_3 P_5$, and so on.

Thus the number of combinations (selections) of 5 players, taken 2 at a time, is 10. We also call this quantity $\binom{5}{2}$ or $_5C_2$.

Let us now consider the problem of the players, when we *are* concerned with the order of each pair. The number of permutations (arrangements) of 5 players, taken 2 at a time, is $_5P_2$ or 20 (see section 10.1), made up as follows:

$$
\begin{array}{ll}
P_1 P_2 & P_2 P_1 \\
P_1 P_3 & P_3 P_1 \\
P_1 P_4 & P_4 P_1 \\
P_1 P_5 & P_5 P_1 \\
P_2 P_3 & P_3 P_2 \\
P_2 P_4 & P_4 P_2 \\
P_2 P_5 & P_5 P_2 \\
P_3 P_4 & P_4 P_3 \\
P_3 P_5 & P_5 P_3 \\
P_4 P_5 & P_5 P_4
\end{array}
$$

Now, the number of permutations of 5 players taken 2 at a time will equal the number of combinations of 5 players taken 2 at a time multiplied by the number of ways of permuting each pair. Therefore,

$$_5P_2 = \binom{5}{2} \times 2!$$

N.B.   20 does equal 10×2

Giving us

$$_5C_2 = \frac{_5P_2}{2!} = \frac{5!}{(5-2)!\,2!}$$

In general:

  The number of different ways of combining (selecting) n different objects, taken r at a time, is:

$$\binom{n}{r} \text{ or } _nC_r \text{ or } \frac{n!}{(n-r)!\,r!}$$

10.3   Permutations of objects not all different

This problem can best be illustrated by considering in how many ways the letters of the word EMERGE can be arranged. Let the Es be distinguished by subscripts—we therefore have the following letters: $E_1, E_2, E_3, M, R,$ and G.

There will be $6 \times 5 \times 4 \times 3 \times 2 \times 1 = 6!$ ways of arranging these letters, but we can arrange the Es amongst themselves in $3 \times 2 \times 1 = 3!$ ways without, in fact, getting a different arrangement of the letters EMERGE. Thus, if we do not distinguish between the Es, we will have 'over-counted' by a factor of $3!$ The number of ways of arranging the letters is consequently $6!/3!(=120)$. There are 120 arrangements of the letters of the word EMERGE.

In general:

  The number of arrangements of n objects (taken all together), when there are p of one kind, q of a second kind, etc., is given by:

$$\text{Number of ways} = \frac{n!}{p!\,q!\dots}$$

10.4   Permutations of objects when repetitions are allowed

Suppose we wish to know the total number of ways of arranging three of the letters of the word FORCE, *repetitions being allowed,* i.e. FFO and RRR, for example, are allowable as well as arrangements like RCF. We can analyse the problem as follows:

Letters available	Spaces available		
	1	2	3
F			
C			
O			
E			
R			

Clearly,   we can fill space 1 in 5 ways,
            we can fill space 2 in 5 ways,
and   we can fill space 3 in 5 ways.

So the total number of arrangements is

$$5 \times 5 \times 5 = 5^3$$

$$= 125$$

There are 125 ways of permuting the letters.

In general :

The number of permutations of n unlike objects, taken r at a time, when repetitions are permitted is given by:

$$\text{Number of ways} = n^r$$

10.5   Some worked examples

In actual problems, especially where various conditions are laid down, it is not always possible to write down a single mathematical expression that will yield the correct answer; often we have to make several separate calculations. It is also very useful sometimes to know that:

$$\binom{n}{r} = \binom{n}{n-r},$$

e.g.

$$\binom{12}{9} = \binom{12}{3}$$

The point is that, in practice, to evaluate a quantity such as $\binom{12}{3}$ quickly, we would think of it not as

$$\frac{12!}{(12-3)!\,3!}$$

but rather as a

$$\frac{12.11.10}{3!}$$

and so on.

Finally, the quantity 0! rather surprisingly equals 1, so that, for example,

$$\binom{4}{4} = \binom{4}{0} = \frac{4!}{(4-0)!\,0!} = 1$$

Example 1:   Find the number of different ways in which all 11 letters of the word 'arrangement' can be permuted.

We have:

$$A\ A\ R\ R\ N\ N\ E\ E\ G\ M\ T$$

Therefore

$$\text{Number of ways} = \frac{11!}{2!\,2!\,2!\,2!}$$

$$= 2\,494\,800$$

There are 2 494 800 ways.

Example 2: Find the number of different ways in which a cricket team, consisting of 11 people, can be chosen from a group of 16.

$$\text{Number of ways} = \binom{16}{11}$$

$$= \binom{16}{5}$$

$$= \frac{16 \cdot 15 \cdot 14 \cdot 13 \cdot 12}{5 \cdot 4 \cdot 3 \cdot 2 \cdot 1}$$

$$= 4368$$

There are 4368 ways.

Example 3: In how many ways may 12 different coins be placed in 17 envelopes, not more than one coin being placed in each? Leave the answer in factorial form.

The first coin can be disposed of in 17 ways.
The second coin can be disposed of in 16 ways, etc.
i.e. the total number of ways $= 17 \times 16 \times \ldots \times 7 \times 6$

$$= 17!/5!$$

There are 17!/5! ways.

Example 4: There are two boxes containing coloured discs. Box I contains a large number of blue and green discs, while Box II contains a large number of blue, green, red, yellow, and white discs. How many different combinations of colours can be made by selecting: (a) one disc from each box, (b) two differently coloured discs from Box II, (c) any two discs from Box I?

(a) If the disc from Box I is blue we have the following possibilities:

BB
BG
BR = 5 combinations
BY
BW

If the disc from Box I is green we have the following possibilities:

(GB) (already counted)
GG
GR $= 4$ combinations
GY
GW

Therefore there are 9 different combinations.

(b) Required value is $\binom{5}{2} = 10$.
There are 10 different combinations.

(c) There are three possibilities: BB, BG or GG.
There are 3 different combinations.

10.6 Probability

Suppose that a particular event, or occurrence, can happen in h ways and fail to happen in f ways, and that each of these $(h + f)$ possibilities is equally likely, then we say:

The *probability, p*, that the event does occur is

$$\frac{h}{h + f}$$

and the *probability, q*, that the event does not occur is

$$\frac{f}{h + f}$$

Now,

$$p + q = \frac{h}{h + f} + \frac{f}{h + f}$$

$$= \frac{h + f}{h + f}$$

$$= 1$$

i.e.
$$p + q = 1$$

It therefore follows that
$$q = 1 - p$$

i.e. if the probability that an event occurs is p, the probability that it does *not* occur is $1 - p$.

N.B.   When an event is certain to happen, $q = 0$, so $p = 1$. Likewise when an event is certain *not* to happen $p = 0$. It also follows that p can only take values between 0 and 1 or, if we use percentages, between 0 and 100 per cent.

Example 1:   What is the probability of throwing a number greater than 4 with a die whose faces are numbered from 1 to 6?

Number of ways the event can happen $= 2$ (a 5 or a 6)
Total number of ways $= 6$

Therefore, probability $= \frac{2}{6} = \frac{1}{3}$

The probability is $\frac{1}{3}$ (or $0.3\dot{3}$ or $33\frac{1}{3}$ per cent).

Example 2:   In a competition a prize is given for correctly forecasting the results of six football matches. If a competitor sends in ten different forecasts, what is the probability, that he receives the prize?

Each of the six matches can have three results: a home win, an away win, or a draw. So,

$$\text{Total number of outcomes} = 3^6 = 729$$

and

$$\text{The number of guesses} = 10$$

Therefore the probability of a correct guess is

$$\frac{10}{729} = 0.013\,72$$

The probability is 0.0137 (or 1.37 per cent).

N.B.   We can see from the above example that the probability that he does *not* receive the prize is $100.00 - 1.37 = 98.63$ per cent, so his chances of success are slim.

10.7   Mutually exclusive events

Suppose we have 16 coloured beads:

> 8 red,
> 5 blue,

and

> 3 green.

Let us consider the probability, p, that we select (at random) either a blue *or* a green bead. Now, since no bead can be blue *and* green, we say that the act of selecting it is a *mutually exclusive event*.

Accordingly, let the probability of selecting a blue bead be p(b) and let the probability of selecting a green bead be p(g), then:

$$p(\text{b}) = \frac{\text{Number of favourable ways}}{\text{Total number of ways}}$$

$$= \tfrac{5}{16}$$

and similarly:

$$p(\text{g}) = \tfrac{3}{16}$$

So the probability, p, that we select either a blue or a green bead is

$$p(b) + p(g) = 5/16 + 3/16$$
$$= 1/2$$

i.e.

$$p = \tfrac{1}{2}$$

We have a simple check on this result, for clearly p(b or g) is

$$\frac{\text{Number of favourable ways}}{\text{Total number of ways}} = \frac{5+3}{16}$$
$$= \tfrac{1}{2} \text{ (as before)}$$

In general:

If E_1 and E_2 are two mutually exclusive events, and the probability that E_1 occurs is $p(E_1)$ and the probability that E_2 occurs is $p(E_2)$, then the probability, p, that either E_1 *or* E_2 occurs is given by:

$$\underline{p = p(E_1) + p(E_2)}$$

10.8   Dependent events

Let us take the 16 coloured beads again, and consider now the probability, p, that 2 beads selected at random should *both* be red. Let the probability of drawing a first red bead be $p(r_1)$, and let the probability of drawing a second red bead be $p(r_2)$.

Now,

$$p(r_1) = \frac{\text{Number of favourable ways}}{\text{Total number of ways}}$$
$$= \tfrac{8}{16}$$

Having obtained our first red bead we are now left with: 7 red, 5 blue, and 3 green beads. Hence

$$p(r_2) = \frac{7}{7+5+3}$$
$$= \tfrac{7}{15}$$

so, the probability, p, that *both* beads are red is

$$p(r_1) \times p(r_2) = \tfrac{8}{16} \times \tfrac{7}{15}$$
$$= \tfrac{56}{240}$$
$$= \tfrac{7}{30}$$
$$p = \tfrac{7}{30}$$

Again, we can check this result, for, the total number of possible red pairs is $\binom{8}{2}$ and the total number of possible pairs is $\binom{16}{2}$, so,

$$p(2 \text{ reds}) = \binom{8}{2} / \binom{16}{2}$$

$$= \frac{8.7}{2!} \Big/ \frac{16.15}{2!}$$

$$= \frac{8.7}{16.15}$$

$$= \tfrac{7}{30} \text{ (as before)}$$

N.B.   If we are allowed to *replace* the first bead before selecting the second, then $p(2 \text{ reds})$ is now

$$\tfrac{8}{16} \times \tfrac{8}{16} = \tfrac{1}{4}$$

In general :

If E_1 and E_2 are two events, and the probability of E_1 occurring is $p(E_1)$ and the probability, *once E_1 has occurred,* of E_2 occurring is $p(E_2)$, then the probability, p, that they should *both* occur is given by:

$$\underline{p = p(E_1) \times p(E_2) \text{ *}}$$

*N.B.   This is sometimes written as $p(E_2 | E_1)$.

10.9   Completely independent events

If two events E_1 and E_2 are completely independent then, as before, the probability, p, that they should both occur will be given by:

$$p = p(E_1) \times p(E_2)$$

N.B.   If the probability that an event occurs is $p(E)$, the probability that it does not occur is sometimes written $p(\bar{E})$.

However, what can we say about the probability that either should occur? This is now possible for the events are quite independent of each other and they are *not* mutually exclusive. In this case it can be shown that the probability, p, that either or both should occur is given by:

$$p(E_1 \cup E_2) = p(E_1) + p(E_2) - p(E_1 \cap E_2).$$

We have to subtract the term $p(E_1 \cap E_2)$ because otherwise it will have been included twice, once with E_1 and once with E_2.

The above equation involves set theory, and since the following examples can be solved without the use of Venn Diagrams, it is proposed to use an alternative method which is simpler to understand.

Example 1:   The probability that a train arrives on time at terminus A is $\tfrac{5}{6}$, while the probability that a train arrives on time at terminus B is $\tfrac{3}{4}$. For two trains selected at random from each system find:
(a) the probability that they both arrive on time,

(b) the probability that only one of them arrives on time,
(c) the probability that neither arrives on time.

(a) We have $p(E_1) = \frac{5}{6}$ and $p(E_2) = \frac{3}{4}$:
so the probability that they both arrive on time is

$$p(E_1) \times p(E_2) = \frac{5}{6} \times \frac{3}{4}$$
$$= \frac{5}{8}.$$

The probability is $\frac{5}{8}$.

(b) Probability that only one arrives on time

$$= p(E_1) \times p(\bar{E}_2) + p(E_2) \times p(\bar{E}_1)$$
$$= (\frac{5}{6} \times \frac{1}{4}) + (\frac{3}{4} \times \frac{1}{6})$$
$$= \frac{5+3}{24} = \frac{1}{3}.$$

The probability is $\frac{1}{3}$.

(c) Here we require the probability that *both* are late. Now, the probability that the first train is late is

$$1 - \frac{5}{6} = \frac{1}{6},$$

So

$$p(\bar{E}_1) = \frac{1}{6}$$

Similarly

$$p(\bar{E}_2) = \frac{1}{4}$$

Thus, the probability that both trains are late is

$$p(\bar{E}_1) \times p(\bar{E}_2) = \frac{1}{6} \times \frac{1}{4}$$
$$= \frac{1}{24}.$$

The probability is $\frac{1}{24}$.

Example 2:   12 different coins are to be placed in 17 envelopes, not more than one coin being placed in each. What is the probability that:
(a)   a particular envelope receives a coin?
(b)   a particular envelope receives a particular coin?
(c)   the last three envelopes remain empty?

(a)   Imagine that we have 12 coins and 5 'non-coins' to place in 17 envelopes, then

$$p = \frac{\text{Number of favourable ways}}{\text{Total number of ways}}$$
$$= \frac{12}{12 + 5}$$
$$= \frac{12}{17}$$

The probability is $\frac{12}{17}$.

(b)   Imagine this time that we have 1 special coin, 11 other coins, and 5 'non-coins':

$$p = \frac{\text{Number of favourable ways}}{\text{Total number of ways}}$$

$$= \frac{1}{1 + 11 + 5}$$

$$= \frac{1}{17}$$

The probability is $\frac{1}{17}$.

(c)   We have 12 coins and 5 'non-coins', therefore the probability of a first envelope receiving a 'non-coin' (i.e. remaining empty) is

$$\frac{5}{5 + 12} = \frac{5}{17}$$

The probability that a second envelope should also receive a 'non-coin' therefore is

$$\tfrac{5}{17} \times \tfrac{4}{16}$$

Accordingly, the probability that *three* envelopes should all be empty is given by:

$$p = \tfrac{5}{17} \times \tfrac{4}{16} \times \tfrac{3}{15}$$

$$= \tfrac{1}{68}.$$

The probability is $\frac{1}{68}$.

Example 3:   A party of 7 children consists of 4 boys and 3 girls. Four of the children are chosen at random from this party.
(a)   Calculate the probability that the 4 selected will contain at least 2 boys.
(b)   If 2 of the children in the original party are brother and sister, what is the probability that the selected group of 4 will not include both?

(a)   Total number of 4s $= \binom{7}{4} = \dfrac{7.6.5}{3.2.1} = 35$

So, selecting *four* children gives

$$p(2 \text{ boys, 2 girls}) = \tfrac{1}{35}\binom{4}{2}\binom{3}{2} = \tfrac{18}{35}$$

$$p(3 \text{ boys, 1 girl}) = \tfrac{1}{35}\binom{4}{3}\binom{3}{1} = \tfrac{12}{35}$$

and

$$p(4 \text{ boys, 0 girl}) = \tfrac{1}{35}\binom{4}{4}\binom{3}{0} = \tfrac{1}{35}$$

Therefore,

$$p(\text{at least 2 boys}) = p(2 \text{ boys, 2 girls}) + p(3 \text{ boys, 1 girl}) + p(4 \text{ boys})$$

$$= \tfrac{18}{35} + \tfrac{12}{35} + \tfrac{1}{35}$$

$$= \tfrac{31}{35}$$

The probability is $\tfrac{31}{35}$.

(b) $p(\text{both not included}) = 1 - p(\text{both included})$

For $p(\text{both included})$, we require brother and sister and any 2 out of 5. So number of 4s including both brother and sister is $\binom{5}{2}$. Therefore,

$$p(\text{both included}) = \tfrac{1}{35}\binom{5}{2}$$

$$= \tfrac{10}{35}$$

$$= \tfrac{2}{7}$$

So,

$$p(\text{both not included}) = 1 - \tfrac{2}{7}$$

$$= \tfrac{5}{7}.$$

The probability is $\tfrac{5}{7}$.

Example 4 :   A student is asked to answer 4 particular questions from an exercise containing 10 questions. He ignores these instructions and answers 6 selected at random. Find the probability that he has answered
(a)   the 4 questions set;
(b)   3 out of the 4 questions set.

(a)   Total number of 6s $= \binom{10}{6}$

$$= \binom{10}{4}$$

$$= 210.$$

Favourable 6s $= 4$ questions set $+$ any 2 out of 6

So,

Number of favourable 6s $= \binom{6}{2}$

Therefore,

$$p = \binom{6}{2}\tfrac{1}{210} = \tfrac{15}{210}$$

$$= \tfrac{1}{14}.$$

The probability is $\tfrac{1}{14}$.

(b)   Favourable 6s $= 3$ out of 4 questions set $+$ any 3 out of 6

So,

Number of favourable 6s $= \binom{4}{3} \times \binom{6}{3}$

$$= 4 \times 20$$

$$= 80$$

Therefore,

$$p = \tfrac{80}{210}$$

$$= \tfrac{8}{21}$$

The probability is $\tfrac{8}{21}$.

Example 5: Two athletes A and B run in the semi-finals of the 400 metres hurdles. The probability of A succeeding in a semi-final is $\tfrac{1}{3}$, the probability of B succeeding in a semi-final is $\tfrac{1}{2}$.

(a) Assuming that they run in different semi-finals calculate the probability that: (i) both A and B reach the final, (ii) at least one of them reaches the final.

(b) If both of them run in the *same* semi-final calculate the probability that neither will reach the final.

(a) (i)

$$p(\text{A and B in final}) = p(\text{A}) \times p(\text{B})$$

$$= \tfrac{1}{3} \times \tfrac{1}{2}$$

$$= \tfrac{1}{6}.$$

The probability is $\tfrac{1}{6}$.

(ii)

$$p(\text{both successful}) = \tfrac{1}{3} \times \tfrac{1}{2}$$

$$= \tfrac{1}{6}$$

$$= p_1$$

$$p(\text{A successful}) \quad = \tfrac{1}{3}$$

Therefore,

$$p(\text{A not successful}) = \tfrac{2}{3}$$

$$p(\text{B successful}) = \tfrac{1}{2}$$

Therefore,

$$p(\text{B not successful}) = \tfrac{1}{2}$$

Therefore,

$$p(\text{A successful, B not successful}) = \tfrac{1}{3} \times \tfrac{1}{2} = \tfrac{1}{6}$$

$$= p_2$$

and

$$p(\text{B successful, A not successful}) = \tfrac{1}{2} \times \tfrac{2}{3} = \tfrac{1}{3}$$

$$= p_3$$

So,

$$p(\text{at least one successful}) = p_1 + p_2 + p_3$$

$$= \tfrac{1}{6} + \tfrac{1}{6} + \tfrac{1}{3}$$

$$= \tfrac{2}{3}$$

The probability is $\tfrac{2}{3}$.

(b) It is not possible to evaluate this probability since the probabilities given are not necessarily independent once A and B compete in the same race. The probabilities of A and B winning if they are in the same race need to be re-assigned, so that all the probabilities involved with that race add to unity.

10.10   Probability and possibility spaces

In certain types of problem, the evaluation of probabilities can be considerably simplified if we make use of what are known as *possibility spaces*. For example, suppose we have two rather unusual dice: a regular dodecahedron, having its pentagonal faces numbered 1 to 12, and a regular tetrahedron, having its triangular faces numbered 1 to 4 (the score of this die is taken to be the number on the bottom or hidden face). Let us further suppose that we wish to know the probability of scoring a total of at least 5, when the dice are thrown together. We proceed as follows: firstly, we construct a *possibility space table*, which is, a table containing all the possible outcomes:

				(B)					(A)		
12 1	11 1	10 1	9 1	8 1	7 1	6 1	5 1	4 1	3 1	2 1	1 1
12 2	11 2	10 2	9 2	8 2	7 2	6 2	5 2	4 2	3 2	2 2	1 2
12 3	11 3	10 3	9 3	8 3	7 3	6 3	5 3	4 3	3 3	2 3	1 3
12 4	11 4	10 4	9 4	8 4	7 4	6 4	5 4	4 4	3 4	2 4	1 4

Secondly, we note that there are 48 possible results, so assuming both die are true and therefore that each of these outcomes is equally likely, the probability of attaining a particular score will be $\frac{1}{48}$.

We now return to our problem: the probability of scoring at least 5 with the dice. It is very easy on our diagram to enclose all those scores which are *under* 5 (see right-hand dashed line (A)). There are in fact six such scores; therefore there are $48-6 = 42$ scores which total at least 5; so: the probability of scoring at least 5 is

$$42 \times \tfrac{1}{48} = \tfrac{7}{8}$$

i.e.

$$p(\geq 5) = \tfrac{7}{8}$$

Similarly, if we wish to find the probability of scoring 9, say, it is again a simple matter to enclose all the allowable possibilities (see left-hand dashed line (B)). This time there are four so that

$$p(9) = 4 \times \tfrac{1}{48}$$
$$= \tfrac{1}{12}$$

i.e.

$$p(9) = \tfrac{1}{12}$$

10.11   The expected value and the variance

If we look again at the above possibility space table, we can use it to work out the probabilities of obtaining all possible scores, i.e. scores ranging from 2 to 16. Thus

$$p(2) = \tfrac{1}{48}$$

$$p(3) = \tfrac{1}{48} + \tfrac{1}{48} = \tfrac{2}{48}$$

$$p(4) = \tfrac{1}{48} + \tfrac{1}{48} + \tfrac{1}{48} = \tfrac{3}{48}$$

$$p(5) = \tfrac{1}{48} + \tfrac{1}{48} + \tfrac{1}{48} + \tfrac{1}{48} = \tfrac{4}{48}$$

and so on.

Accordingly, we finish up with the following *discrete probability distribution*:

x	$p(x)$	x	$p(x)$
2	$\tfrac{1}{48}$	10	$\tfrac{4}{48}$
3	$\tfrac{2}{48}$	11	$\tfrac{4}{48}$
4	$\tfrac{3}{48}$	12	$\tfrac{4}{48}$
5	$\tfrac{4}{48}$	13	$\tfrac{4}{48}$
6	$\tfrac{4}{48}$	14	$\tfrac{3}{48}$
7	$\tfrac{4}{48}$	15	$\tfrac{2}{48}$
8	$\tfrac{4}{48}$	16	$\tfrac{1}{48}$
9	$\tfrac{4}{48}$		

Now, if we performed the experiment of throwing the dice a very large number of times, on average, for every 48 throws, we would expect to obtain the following discrete frequency distribution:

x	f	x	f
2	1	10	4
3	2	11	4
4	3	12	4
5	4	13	4
6	4	14	3
7	4	15	2
8	4	16	1
9	4		

We call the mean of the above type of distribution the *expected value* and, because of the perfect symmetry here, it is not difficult to see that the expected value is in fact 9. To confirm this we can calculate $\bar{x}$ in the usual way, by using:

$$\bar{x} = \frac{\sum fx}{\sum f}$$

i.e.

$$\bar{x} = \frac{\begin{array}{c} 1 \times 2 + 2 \times 3 + 3 \times 4 + 4 \times 5 + 4 \times 6 + 4 \times 7 + 4 \times 8 + 4 \times 9 + 4 \times 10 \\ + 4 \times 11 + 4 \times 12 + 4 \times 13 + 3 \times 14 + 2 \times 15 + 1 \times 16 \end{array}}{1 + 2 + 3 + 4 + 4 + 4 + 4 + 4 + 4 + 4 + 4 + 4 + 3 + 2 + 1}$$

$$= \frac{432}{48} = 9 \ ;$$

Thus

$$\bar{x} = 9$$

In Chapter 12 this problem is considered in terms of probability.

Of course, if there is not perfect symmetry the formula method must be used.

We can also work out the variance (and hence the standard deviation) of the above distribution in the usual manner:

x	$d (= x - \bar{x})$	f	d^2	x	d	f	d^2
2	-7	1	49	10	1	4	1
3	-6	2	36	11	2	4	4
4	-5	3	25	12	3	4	9
5	-4	4	16	13	4	4	16
6	-3	4	9	14	5	3	25
7	-2	4	4	15	6	2	36
8	-1	4	1	16	7	1	49
9	0	4	0				

Since variance, $s^2 = \dfrac{\sum fd^2}{\sum f}$, we have

$$s^2 = \frac{49 + 72 + 75 + 64 + 36 + 16 + 4 + 0 + 4 + 16 + 36 + 64 + 75 + 72 + 49}{48}$$

$$= \frac{632}{48} = 13.2 \text{ (correct to one decimal place)}$$

So, the standard deviation, $s = \sqrt{13.2} = 3.6$ (correct to one decimal place).

To summarize our results:

Expected value = 9 ; variance = 13.2 ; standard deviation = 3.6.

10.12   Tree diagrams

In some cases, when trying to estimate probabilities, it is helpful to draw what is known as a *tree diagram*. This type of diagram is intended to show all possible outcomes of a particular experiment. Let us illustrate this by means of a simple example. Suppose we have two boxes: Box I containing 3 envelopes and Box II containing 2 tins. In the first envelope are 2 red, 2 green, and 1 yellow disc, in the second envelope 1 red and 3 green discs, and in the third envelope 1 red, 1 green, and 1 yellow disc. In the first tin are 3 red discs, while in the second tin there are 2 green and 2 yellow discs.

The experiment consists in choosing one of the two boxes, selecting an envelope or tin at random, and from the latter picking out one disc; the tree diagram for this experiment would be as shown in Figure 10.1.

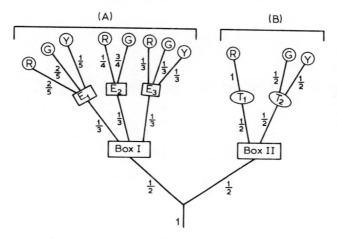

Figure 10.1

Also shown in Figure 10.1 are the probabilities associated with each branch of the tree. Having done this we can work out, for example, the probability that the chosen disc is a red one, i.e.

$$p(\text{red disc}) = \tfrac{1}{2} \times \tfrac{1}{3} \times \tfrac{2}{5} + \tfrac{1}{2} \times \tfrac{1}{3} \times \tfrac{1}{4} + \tfrac{1}{2} \times \tfrac{1}{3} \times \tfrac{1}{3} \text{ (branch system (A))}$$

$$+ \tfrac{1}{2} \times \tfrac{1}{2} \times 1 + \tfrac{1}{2} \times \tfrac{1}{2} \times 0 \text{ (branch system (B))}$$

i.e.

$$p(\text{red disc}) = (\tfrac{1}{15} + \tfrac{1}{24} + \tfrac{1}{18}) + (\tfrac{1}{4} + 0)$$

$$= \tfrac{149}{360}$$

$\underline{p(\text{red disc}) = \tfrac{149}{360}.}$

Once again we can check this result. Since we are bound to obtain either a red, green or yellow disc, it follows that:

$$p(\text{red disc}) + p(\text{green disc}) + p(\text{yellow disc}) = 1$$

now

$$p(\text{green disc}) = \tfrac{1}{2} \times \tfrac{1}{3} \times \tfrac{2}{5} + \tfrac{1}{2} \times \tfrac{1}{3} \times \tfrac{3}{4} + \tfrac{1}{2} \times \tfrac{1}{3} \times \tfrac{1}{3}$$
$$+ \tfrac{1}{2} \times \tfrac{1}{2} \times 0 + \tfrac{1}{2} \times \tfrac{1}{2} \times \tfrac{1}{2}$$

i.e.

$$p(\text{green disc}) = \tfrac{67}{180}$$

While

$$p(\text{yellow disc}) = \tfrac{1}{2} \times \tfrac{1}{3} \times \tfrac{1}{5} + \tfrac{1}{2} \times \tfrac{1}{3} \times 0 + \tfrac{1}{2} \times \tfrac{1}{3} \times \tfrac{1}{3}$$
$$+ \tfrac{1}{2} \times \tfrac{1}{2} \times 0 + \tfrac{1}{2} \times \tfrac{1}{2} \times \tfrac{1}{2}$$

i.e.

$$p(\text{yellow disc}) = \tfrac{77}{360}$$

Thus

$$p(\text{red disc}) + p(\text{green disc}) + p(\text{yellow disc}) = \tfrac{149}{360} + \tfrac{67}{180} + \tfrac{77}{360}$$
$$= \tfrac{149}{360} + \tfrac{134}{360} + \tfrac{77}{360}$$
$$= \tfrac{360}{360}$$
$$= 1$$

which checks, indicating that our result for the red disc is correct.

Exercise 10

1. (a) Find the number of different ways in which a tennis team consisting of 6 people can be chosen from a group of 10 people.
    (b) Find the number of different ways in which all eight letters of the word SAUSAGES can be arranged.
    (c) Find the number of different ways in which a gold, a silver, and a bronze medal can be awarded to 15 competitors if each competitor can win only one medal. Find also the probability that two particular competitors will both win a medal assuming that all competitors have the same chance of winning each medal.

    (L.U.)

2. (a) In how many different ways may 10 different letters be placed in 15 different boxes, not more than one letter being placed in any box? You may leave the answer in factor form.
    (b) What is the probability that a particular box receives a letter?
    (c) What is the probability that a particular box receives a particular letter?
    (d) What is the probability that the first two boxes remain empty?

    (L.U.)

3. A householder pays a premium of £40 per year to insure the contents of his house against fire and theft. It is estimated that the probability of fire in the year is 1 in 104 with expected damage £2000, and the probability of theft is 2 in 103 with expected loss of £400. What is the expected value of the profit (premiums received less expected pay-out) of the company?
    (b) Two fair dice each have faces labelled 1 to 6 in the normal way. One die has the faces 1 and 2 coloured red, the second has faces 1, 2, 3, and 4 coloured red, whilst all other faces are white.

    Calculate the probability of the following events (i) the sum of the scores is even, (ii) both faces are red. Show that these events are independent.

    (L.U.)

4. Sid and Tom are twins and are due to run in the heats of the 100 metres sprint. Only the winners of each heat run in the final. Assuming that the probability of Sid winning any heat in which he runs a 1/4, whilst for Tom it is 1/5, calculate the probability that
    (a) Sid and Tom both run in the final, assuming that they run in different heats,
    (b) at least one of the twins runs in the final, assuming that they run in different heats,
    (c) neither of them runs in the final, assuming that they run in the same heat.

    (L.U.)

5. A do-it-yourself enthusiast has two boxes. One contains many plugs of sizes 6, 8, and 10 in equal numbers. The second contains many screws of sizes 4, 6, 8, and 10 in equal numbers.
    (a) How many different combinations of sizes can be made by selecting (i) one screw and one plug, (ii) two screws of different sizes, (iii) any two plugs?
    (b) If he selects a screw and a plug at random, calculate the probability that they are of the same size.

    (L.U.)

6. (a) A student is asked to do three questions from an exercise containing eight questions. How many different selections are possible?
    (b) A student, asked to do three particular questions from an exercise containing eight questions, ignores these instructions and answers four questions selected at random. Find the probability that he has answered (i) all three questions set, (ii) exactly two of three questions set, assuming that all combinations were equally likely to be selected.

    (L.U.)

7. In an experiment two dice are thrown and their scores added. Each die consists of an ordinary die in which the six has been replaced by a one.
    Calculate the probability that
    (a) the score is four,
    (b) the score is not more than six,
    (c) one and only one of the dice shows a five,
    (d) the total score is neither three nor seven.

    (L.U.)

8. A party of nine people consists of five men and four women, and a group of four people is to be chosen at random from this party.
    (a) In a how many ways can a group of four be chosen that contains at least three women? Hence calculate the probability that the four selected will contain at least three women.
    (b) If Mr and Mrs A are included in the original party of nine, what is the probability that the selected group of four will not include both Mr and Mrs A?

    (L.U.)

9. P is an ordinary cubical die and Q is a four faced die in the shape of a regular tetrahedron, the faces carrying the numbers 1, 2, 3, and 4. When Q is thrown the face in contact with the table indicates the score to be counted. In an experiment both dice are thrown simultaneously and their total score, x, is found.
    (a) Construct a table showing the possibility space. Hence calculate the probability of obtaining each possible value of x.
    (b) Calculate the expected value and the variance of x for this probability distribution.

    (L.U.)

10. (a) Each of four bags contains three coloured discs, two red and one green. A disc is

drawn at random from each bag. Find the probability that (i) four red discs are chosen, (ii) two red discs and two green discs are chosen.

(b) There are three bags labelled A, B, and C containing coloured balls. Bag A contains one pink ball, three yellow balls, and two blue balls; bag B contains three pink and two yellow balls; and bag C contains one pink ball, one yellow ball, and three blue balls.

A bag is chosen at random and from that bag a ball is chosen at random. Construct a tree diagram showing all possible outcomes. Calculate the probability that a yellow ball is chosen.

(L.U.)

11. An ordinary fair cubical die with faces numbered 1, 2, 3, 4, 5, and 6 respectively is thrown four times. Calculate the probabilities that
(a) the score on the first throw will be 6 and the score on the second throw will not be 6,
(b) all four scores will be even,
(c) exactly two 6s will be thrown,
(d) the sum of four scores will exceed 5.

(J.M.B.)

12. (a) Evaluate $_{12}P_3$ and $\binom{8}{5}$.
(b) Four cards are selected at random from a normal pack of 52. (i) How many possible selections of four cards are there? (ii) What is the probability that all four cards are diamonds? (iii) What is the probability that the four cards will differ only in suit? (iv) In how many different ways can four aces be arranged when held in the hand?
(c) A player deals two cards at random from a normal pack of 52. What is the probability that they are an ace and a picture card given that the first card is (i) an ace, (ii) a picture card?

(A.E.B.)

13. (a) Six people are going on a motoring holiday in a six-seater car. In how many ways can they be seated if (i) all six are able to drive, (ii) the owner of the car insists on driving, (iii) the owner of the car is to drive and his wife is to sit next to him?

When the party stops for refreshments, two people are required to go to purchase them. In how many ways can these two people be selected?
(b) In the directory of a certain large telephone exchange, 15 per cent of the subscribers are named Smith, 12 per cent Jones, 8 per cent Brown, and 7 per cent Thomas. If, at the exchange, a connection is set up at random, calculate the probability that (i) both subscribers would be called Smith, (ii) just one of the subscribers would be called Jones, (iii) at least one of the subscribers would be called Brown, (iv) neither of the subscribers would be called Thomas, (v) a Smith would be connected to a Brown.

(A.E.B.)

14. Expand $(H + T)^4$.
(a) If 4 coins are tossed at the same time, find the probability that (i) 4 heads will appear, (ii) 2 heads and 2 tails will appear.
(b) From a class of 20 boys a rugby team of 15 boys is chosen for a number of games by drawing names for each game from a hat. Calculate the probability that a particular boy (i) is chosen for the first game, (ii) is not chosen for the first game, (iii) is not chosen for the first game and is not chosen for the second game but is chosen for the the third game.

(O. & C.)

15. (a) Three hockey games are to be played by a school team at a festival. Assuming that a win, a draw or a loss are all equally probable, calculate, by a tree diagram or otherwise, the probability that (i) all three games will be won, (ii) one will be won, one lost and one drawn, (iii) two will be drawn and one lost.

(b) The 13 cards of a suit of playing cards are placed face downwards on a table. Calculate the probability that in three consecutive random selections (i) cards numbered 6, 7, 8 are selected in that order, (ii) cards numbered 6, 7, 8 are selected in any order.

(O. & C.)

16. (a) To commence a certain game a player must score a *total* of either 2 or 5 or 7 from *two* throws of a fair die. Which of these scores is most likely to occur? Give a reason for your answer.

(b) Three men, A, B, and C, shoot at a target. The probabilities of each hitting the target are $\frac{1}{3}$, $\frac{1}{4}$, and $\frac{1}{6}$, respectively. Find: (i) the probability that A is the only man to hit the target, (ii) the probability that *exactly* one man hits the target.

(N.I.)

17. (a) A class wishes to find the probability of obtaining exactly two heads when a fair coin is tossed three times. Describe an experiment which you could carry out to estimate this probability. Your answer should describe clearly (i) how the data is recorded as the experiment proceeds, (ii) how this data is used to estimate the probability.

(b) As a result of such an experiment a class concludes that the probability of obtaining exactly two heads is 0.4. By drawing a tree diagram, or otherwise, show that the exact probability is 0.375.

Give the most likely reason why the experimental result is not a better estimate and suggest how the class might try to improve it.

(N.I.)

18. The probability that a golfer sinks a putt is $\frac{2}{3}$. Find the probability that, of three similar putts, the golfer sinks (a) all three, (b) less than three, (c) at least two.

(A.E.B.)

19. A die, with faces numbered 1 to 6, is biased in such a way that on throwing it the number shown on the uppermost face is twice as likely to be an even number as an odd number. Find the probability
(a) that, on throwing the die once, an odd number appears on the uppermost face,
(b) that, on throwing the die twice, the sum of the two numbers appearing on the uppermost face is odd.

(A.E.B.)

20. A bag contains 100 beads of which 30 are white. If two beads are drawn simultaneously from the bag, calculate the probability that at least one bead is white.

(A.E.B.)

21. In a certain game of chance, two common six-sided dice are thrown simultaneously and the score obtained is the sum of the two numbers shown by the dice.
(a) Assuming the two dice to be unbiased, calculate the probability of each of the possible scores, giving your answers clearly in a table.
(b) If the two dice are thrown once only, what is the most probable score?
(c) If the two dice are thrown twice, what is the probability that both scores will be 5?
(d) If the two dice are thrown three times, what is the probability that none of the scores will be 7?
(e) If the dice are thrown 108 times, what is the most probable number of times that the score will be 8?
(f) Two other dice were thrown 72 times and the scores obtained were as follows:

Score	7	8	9	10	11	12
Frequency	11	13	12	10	14	12

Write down the expected frequencies for 72 throws of two unbiased dice. Compare the two distributions and suggest a possible explanation for the difference.

(A.E.B.)

22. For a certain card game, a normal pack of 52 cards is taken and all the twos, threes, and fours are removed, leaving a reduced pack of 40 cards. An Ace scores 11, the picture cards (King, Queen, and Jack) score 10, while the other cards score their face value. Each player receives two cards, the total score being the sum of the scores of the two cards.

(a) A player is dealt two cards, a heart and a spade, from this reduced pack. Produce a table showing the total scores of all the possible pairs of cards which the player could have received and hence find (i) the most probable score, (ii) the probability that the player has two picture cards, (iii) the probability that his score is exactly 15, (iv) the probability that his score is 15 or less.

(b) If instead the player received two hearts, use the appropiate portion of your table to find (i) the most probable score, (ii) the probability that the player has two picture cards, (iii) the probability that his score is exactly 15, (iv) the probability that his score is 15 or less.

(A.E.B.)

11
Errors and approximations

11.1 Errors in measurement

Suppose we are told that a cube has sides two centimetres long. Can we assume that the volume of the cube is, in consequence, eight cubic centimetres precisely?

Let us examine what we mean when we say that the length of something is, for instance, two centimetres. Do we mean that the length is *exactly* two centimetres? If so, we are implying that the length is 2.000 000 000 recurring and further: *that the instrument used is capable of measuring to an infinite number of decimal places*! Obviously this is absurd and commonsense tells us that even using a very sensitive length-measuring instrument, such as a micrometer screw-gauge, we cannot possibly measure more accurately than to about one hundredth part of a millimetre or to one thousandth part of a centimetre.

Now, let us suppose that the cube has been measured with a micrometer screw-gauge. Then, if we say that each side of the cube measures two centimetres all we are really claiming is that each side measures 2.000 centimetres, correct to three decimal places. In addition there is an uncertainty factor which means that we can only give a *range* of values for this measurement.

Let us try and illustrate this. Suppose the cube really *does* have a side exactly 2 cm long, then our micrometer screw-gauge will measure it as 2.000 cm. Suppose *another* cube actually has a side of length 2.000 49 cm, then our micrometer screw-gauge (which is *not* accurate to one ten-thousandth of a centimetre) will still register the length as 2.000 cm. Similarly, if the length is exactly 1.999 50 cm, our measuring instrument will once again register 2.000 cm. Therefore, when we say that the length is 2.000 cm what we mean is that it lies somewhere in the range 1.999 50 cm to 2.000 49 cm, hence the uncertainty factor mentioned above.

Now, the quantity 2.000 49 is, to all intents and purposes, equal to 2.0005. So, we can modify the original range given above and summarize as follows: if we use an instrument that can measure accurately to within 0.001 cm, and obtain a length of 2.000 cm, the latter lies somewhere in the range 1.9995 to

2.0005 cm, or we can say that the length is 2.000 ± 0.0005 cm. This is basically why *errors* will normally occur whenever we set out to 'measure' something.

Let us now revert to the question concerning the *volume* of the cube. Each side of the cube is 2.000 cm; i.e. each side of the cube lies within the range 1.9995 to 2.0005 cm. Therefore, the *smallest* volume the cube can have will be:

$$1.9995 \times 1.9995 \times 1.9995 = 7.9940 \text{ cubic centimetres (cm}^3\text{)}$$

the *greatest* volume the cube can have will be:

$$2.0005 \times 2.0005 \times 2.0005 = 8.0060 \text{ cm}^3$$

Thus, we do *not* know the volume of the cube with certainty, any more than we knew its length with certainty. All we can really say is that the volume lies somewhere in the range 7.9940 to 8.0060 cm^3, or that it is 8 ± 0.006 cm^3.

Example: A farmer knows that the total area available for sowing wheat is 75 hectares (to the nearest hectare). At the completion of the harvest he has the following additional information:

(a) He has obtained 1.5 tonnes of wheat per hectare (to the nearest half tonne).

(b) There are 1000 kilograms in one tonne.

Estimate (in kilograms) between what limits his production lies (to the nearest 100 kg).

Area: this can be anything in the range 74.5–75.5.

Tonnes per hectare: this can be anything in the range 1.25–1.75.

Now, if he had exactly 75 hectares, and the yield was exactly 1.5 tonnes per hectare, his yield in kilograms would be:

$$\text{Yield} = 75 \times 1.5 \times 1000 \text{ kg}$$

and, from the figures above, it is clear that his minimum yield will be:

$$\text{Yield (min.)} = 74.5 \times 1.25 \times 1000 \text{ kg} = 93\,125 \text{ kg}$$

and, similarly,

$$\text{Yield (max.)} = 75.5 \times 1.75 \times 1000 \text{ kg} = 132\,125 \text{ kg}$$

N.B.   Anything below 74.5 rounds down to 74, whilst anything above 75.5 rounds up to 76, etc.

His production lies somewhere in the range: $93\,100 - 132\,100$ kg.

The reader will see that because of uncertainties in the original data, the farmer is uncertain of his production to the extent of some 39 000 kg or nearly 39 tonnes!

This illustrates the dilemma of anyone trying to estimate a value. If their calculation involves three, four, or even more variables and none of these is known with certainty, then, as the above example clearly shows, there can be a disturbingly large range of possible answers.

11.2   Percentage error

This is an important quantity and is defined as follows:

$$\text{Percentage error} = \frac{\text{Absolute error} \times 100}{\text{True value}}$$

where

$$\text{Absolute (or actual) error} = \text{Measured value} - \text{True value}$$

N.B.   A percentage error can be $+$ or $-$.

Example: A rod is known to have a diameter of 5 mm. It is measured with a micrometer screw-gauge and the diameter is recorded as 4.992 mm. What is the percentage error in this measurement?

We have:

$$\text{Measured value} = 4.992$$
$$\text{True value} = 5.000;$$

Therefore,

$$\text{Actual error} = 4.992 - 5.000$$
$$= -0.008$$

$$\text{Percentage error} = \frac{\text{Absolute error} \times 100}{\text{True value}}, \text{ so here}:$$

$$\text{Percentage error} = \frac{(-0.008) \times 100}{5}$$
$$= -0.16.$$

The percentage error is -0.16.

11.3   Relative error

This quantity is not used as much as the percentage error; it is closely related to the latter, however, for:

$$\text{Relative error} = \frac{\text{Absolute error}}{\text{True value}}$$

Thus, in the example above the relative error would simply be:

$$\text{Relative error} = \frac{(4.992 - 5.000)}{5}$$
$$= -0.0016$$

Notice once again that a relative error can be positive or negative.

11.4   Approximations

In many ways this is one of the most important and useful topics in statistics. All of us, every day of our lives, continuously make approximations. If someone asks us how long it will take to walk to the village shop, we give a reply like: 'Oh, *about* ten minutes'. We do *not* say 'Oh, nine minutes fifty-two seconds', firstly, because it is very unlikely that we could predict with this degree of accuracy how long it would take some-one else (even if it were the average time for us) and secondly, because *they do not require this degree of accuracy.*

Consider, for a moment, the case of a cinema-manager who is studying the daily attendances at his theatre for a one-week period. Let us suppose that he has the following figures:

Daily Attendances Period: Mon. 25 Feb. to Sun. 3 March inc.

Mon.	Tues.	Wed.	Thurs.	Fri.	Sat.	Sun.
75	68	103	100	228	301	214

Total attendance for week: 1089

Now, supposing he was asked to summarize this information over the phone to his head office. Would he need to remember these figures exactly or could he round them all off to the nearest 10 say, without introducing any serious error? Let us put it to the test:

Daily Attendance (to the nearest 10)

Mon.	Tues.	Wed.	Thurs.	Fri.	Sat.	Sun.
80	70	100	100	230	300	210

Approximate total attendance for week: 1090

Note that, despite rounding off to the nearest 10, our final total is only 1 out in 1089. In other words our percentage error is:

$$\frac{(1090 - 1089) \times 100}{1089} \simeq +0.09$$

or we can say that our estimate is 99.9 per cent accurate, which is exceptionally good, and better than generally required.

When we round off figures in the above way (that is to say systematically), we obtain *unbiased approximations*, and providing we proceed with caution and think carefully about whether we should be rounding off to the nearest 0.1, 10, 100 or 1000, and so on, we usually obtain a satisfactory estimate. If, however, we start rounding-off in an *unsystematic* manner, then we are likely to get much poorer results. We will in fact obtain a *biased approximation* and to illustrate this let us return to the data concerning cinema attendances. This time we will take the daily figures and round them all *down* to the nearest 10:

Daily Attendances (*rounded down to the nearest* 10)

Mon.	Tues.	Wed.	Thurs.	Fri.	Sat.	Sun.
70	60	100	100	220	300	210

'Approximate' total attendance for week: 1060

Not so good this time! Let us look at our percentage error again:

$$\text{Percentage error} = \frac{(1060 - 1089) \times 100}{1089} = -2.7$$

thus we are nearly 30 times more inaccurate than when we used unbiased approximations.

Exercise 11

1. A solid rectangular block has a square base whose edge is measured to be of length 6.5 cm while the height of the block is measured as 8.0 cm. What do these measurements imply with regard to the limits of
   (a) the perimeter of the base,
   (b) the volume of the block?

   (A.E.B.)

2. Find the limits of the following decimal fraction if the numbers are rounded off to the first decimal place.

   $$\frac{3.7 \times 1.2}{2.1}$$

   (A.E.B.)

3. The figures in the calculation $\frac{3 \times 2}{5}$ are given correct to the nearest integer. What is the smallest value of the result, correct to two decimal places?
   A. 0.68.
   B. 0.83.
   C. 1.20.
   D. 1.59.

   (A.E.B.)

4. Two numbers are given correct to three significant figures as 11.6 and 16.7. To how many significant figures can their sum be guaranteed?
   A. 1.
   B. 2.
   C. 3.
   D. 4.

   (A.E.B.)

5. State between what limits the following product lies if the numbers have been rounded off as shown.

   $$5.63 \times 4.41$$

6. State between what limits the following quotient lies if the numbers have been rounded off as shown.

   $$5.41 \div 4.63$$

7. The true value of a constant is known to be 3.142. If some-one claims the measurement to be 3.100 what is
   (a) the absolute error,

   (b) the relative error,
   (c) the percentage error?

8. State between what limits the following product lies if the numbers have been rounded off to the given significant figures:

$$4.1 \times 2.7 \times 3.9$$

Give your answer correct to the nearest integer.

9. State between what limits the following lies:

$$\frac{2.6 \times 3.4}{1.2}$$

Give your answer to the same degree of accuracy as the question.

10. The lengths of a number of machine components were recorded as follows:

Length (cm)	Number of components
20–	2
22–	4
24–	7
etc.	etc.

State the limits between which the actual lengths of the 4 components in the second class must lie if lengths were measured (a) to the nearest cm, (b) to the nearest mm.

(A.E.B.)

11. A motorist notes that, according to the clock and the distance-measuring instrument in his car, he has taken 1 hour to drive 50 km. He concludes that his average speed was 50 km/h. If each of his instruments is accurate to 1 per cent only, between what limits does his true average speed lie?

(A.E.B.)

12. What is the lower limit to the following calculation if the numbers are given in significant figures?

$$\frac{3.8 \times 2.9}{1.2}$$

(A.E.B.)

13. The percentage errors in two numbers x and y are a and b respectively. Show that, if these errors are small, the greatest percentage error in the product xy is approximately $a + b$.

(A.E.B.)

14. Bigville United recorded the following gates at 10 successive home games:

   4275   9300   2295   1412   1152   1695   1282   1037   3475   and 1351

(a) Make an unbiased approximation, to the nearest 100, of the total attendance for all 10 matches.
(b) Make a biased approximation, to the nearest 100, rounding down.
(c) Calculate the percentage error involved in *both* approximations.

15. A total of 1248 tonnes of iron ore was produced in a certain month by 12 miners. Ten of the miners worked for 22 days and the remaining two worked for 20 days. Calculate the average output per man per day worked. Find the percentage error made by a person who calculates the average output per man per day worked by assuming that each of the men worked for 20 days.

(J.M.B.)

16. It is estimated that the population of a certain town is 17 000, to the nearest thousand, and that each inhabitant requires on average 125 litres of water per day, to the nearest litre. Calculate the upper and lower limits of the annual consumption of water of the whole town.

(A.E.B.)

17. If the sides of a rectangle are measured as 5.00 m and 2.00 m calculate the greatest and least possible values of (a) the perimeter, (b) the area.

   Explain the meaning of the terms absolute error and relative error. State the greatest relative error in the smaller of the original measurements and the greatest absolute error for the perimeter.

(A.E.B.)

18. A man runs 1500 metres in 250 seconds. If both these quantities are accurate to 1 per cent between what limits does his average speed lie?

(A.E.B.)

19. The specification for a rectangular enclosure stated that it must be 30 metres by 40 metres, both measured to the nearest metre. Calculate (a) the maximum length of boundary fencing, (b) the minimum area enclosed, to the nearest m^2, each of which would be consistent with the specification.

20. Correct to the nearest whole number, the value of x is 2 and the value of y is 1. Calculate the greatest possible value of each of the expressions (a) $\dfrac{x}{y}$, (b) $\dfrac{y}{(7y - x)}$.

(A.E.B.)

12

The binomial and normal distributions; confidence and significance

12.1   The binomial distribution for a discrete variable

Consider the following hypothetical situation: we have a perfectly fair coin which we are going to toss ten times – we wish to know the probability, each time we perform the experiment, of getting no tails, one tail, two tails, ..., ten tails. Let us try and deal with each of these problems in turn.

1.   The probability of getting no tails
Here, the result of our experiment *has* to be:

$$H\ H\ H\ H\ H\ H\ H\ H\ H\ H$$

Now the probability, p, of getting a tail with a *single* toss is $\frac{1}{2}$, so the probability $p(0)$ of obtaining no tails in *ten* tosses will be given by:

$$p(0) = (\tfrac{1}{2})^{10} \quad \text{or} \quad \tfrac{1}{1024}$$

$(\tfrac{1}{2})^{10}$ can be written as $\binom{10}{0}(\tfrac{1}{2})^{0}(\tfrac{1}{2})^{10}$ and the reason for doing this should become apparent shortly.

2.   The probability of getting one tail
Here, the result of our experiment *could* be:

$$H\ H\ H\ H\ H\ H\ T\ H\ H\ H$$

although it could equally well have been:

$$H\ H\ T\ H\ H\ H\ H\ H\ H\ H$$

The probability, q, of *not* getting a tail with a single toss will be given by:

$$q = 1 - p$$
$$= 1 - \tfrac{1}{2}$$
$$= \tfrac{1}{2}$$

so in this particular experiment, if we regard the achievement of a tail as representing *success*, and the achievement of a head as representing *failure*, we have throughout that:

$$p(\text{success}) = p(\text{failure}) = \tfrac{1}{2}$$

Let us now proceed to calculate the probability $p(1)$ of obtaining just one tail:

$$p(1) = (\tfrac{1}{2})^{10} \times 10$$

because the one tail (see above) can be placed in any one of *ten* positions, so:

$$p(1) = (\tfrac{1}{2})^{10} \times 10 \quad \text{or} \quad \tfrac{10}{1024}$$

However, $(\tfrac{1}{2})^{10} \times 10$ can also be written in the form

$$\binom{10}{1}(\tfrac{1}{2})^{1}(\tfrac{1}{2})^{9}.$$

3. The probability of getting two tails
Possibilities here are:

H T H H H H T H H H   or   T H H H H H H H T H,

and we can clearly say that:

$$p(2) = \binom{10}{2}(\tfrac{1}{2})^{2}(\tfrac{1}{2})^{8} \quad \text{or} \quad \tfrac{45}{1024}$$

N.B. $\binom{10}{2}$ is equivalent to the number of ways of arranging 10 objects, when 8 are of one kind and 2 are of another.

In precisely the same sort of way we can show that:

$$p(3) = \binom{10}{3}(\tfrac{1}{2})^{3}(\tfrac{1}{2})^{7} \quad \text{or} \quad \tfrac{120}{1024}$$

$$p(4) = \binom{10}{4}(\tfrac{1}{2})^{4}(\tfrac{1}{2})^{6} \quad \text{or} \quad \tfrac{210}{1024}$$

right up to

$$p(10) = \binom{10}{10}(\tfrac{1}{2})^{10}(\tfrac{1}{2})^{0}$$

In general, then, if we conduct n trials of an experiment where the chance of success each time is p and the chance of failure each time is q, the probability $p(x)$ of achieving x successes in the n trials is given by:

$$\underline{p(x) = \binom{n}{x}p^{x}q^{n-x} \quad (\text{where } q = 1 - p)}$$

This is the binomial distribution of probabilities for a discrete or discontinuous variable.

Before we proceed any further, a brief explanation of why the term *binomial distribution* is used, ought to be given. The *Binomial Theorem* states in one of its forms that the expansion of

$$(p + q)^{n} = \binom{n}{0}p^{n}q^{0} + \binom{n}{1}p^{n-1}q^{1} + \binom{n}{2}p^{n-2}q^{2} + \ldots + \binom{n}{n}p^{0}q^{n}$$

and the terms on the right-hand side of this equation are precisely the same as those for the probabilities of achieving 0 successes in n trials, 1 success,

2 successes, and so on, when the probability of individual success or failure is p and q respectively.

Let us now list all the probabilities involved in the coin-tossing experiment. We have the following results:

Fair Coin-tossing Experiment: 10 *Tosses*

Numbers of tails, x	Probability, p(x)
0	$\frac{1}{1024}$
1	$\frac{10}{1024}$
2	$\frac{45}{1024}$
3	$\frac{120}{1024}$
4	$\frac{210}{1024}$
5	$\frac{252}{1024}$
6	$\frac{210}{1024}$
7	$\frac{120}{1024}$
8	$\frac{45}{1024}$
9	$\frac{10}{1024}$
10	$\frac{1}{1024}$

The first thing to notice from this table is that

$$p(0) + p(1) + p(2) + \ldots + p(10) = \tfrac{1}{1024} + \tfrac{10}{1024} + \tfrac{45}{1024} + \ldots + \tfrac{1}{1024}$$
$$= \tfrac{1024}{1024}$$
$$= 1$$

This, of course, must be so since in a single run of the experiment we *must* obtain some number of tails in the range 0 to 10.

Secondly, we can see that *the most likely* result is that we should obtain 5 tails and 5 heads, for $p(5)$ is greater than any of the other individual probabilities. Our own commonsense reinforces this result.

Now suppose that we conduct our experiment not once but 1024 times. We would then expect to get the following results:

0	tail	or	10	tails – once		
1	tail	or	9	tails – 10	times
2	tails	or	8	tails – 45	times
3	tails	or	7	tails – 120	times
4	tails	or	6	tails – 210	times
5	tails	and	5	heads – 252	times

If we plot their results on a *line chart* we get Figure 12.1.

Alternatively, we can plot the results as a *histogram* (Figure 12.2), regarding 2 tails, for example, as encompassing everything in the range 1.5–2.5, and so on. *N.B.* In both Figures 12.1 and 12.2 the envelope of the lines or rectangles follow a smooth, bell-like curve.

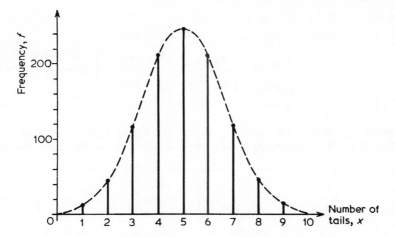

Figure 12.1 Frequencies to be expected (1024 experiments)

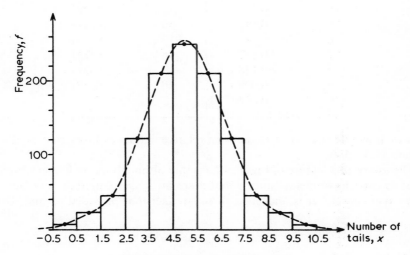

Figure 12.2 Expected frequencies

Now consider an experiment where we have three coloured beads: one blue, one green, and one yellow. These are contained in a box and the experiment consists of selecting a bead at random, replacing it, thoroughly shaking the beads once more, and then repeating the process. Altogether we will conduct the experiment twenty times and then construct the corresponding *bionomial probability distribution*. In our experiment the selection of the green bead will count as a success, whilst either of the other beads will count as a failure. In a single experiment it is clear that

$$p = \tfrac{1}{3} \quad \text{and} \quad q(= 1 - p) = \tfrac{2}{3}$$

Using the formula $p(x) = \binom{n}{x}p^x q^{n-x}$, we get

$$p(0g) = \binom{20}{0}(\tfrac{1}{3})^0(\tfrac{2}{3})^{20-0} = 0.000$$
$$p(1g) = \binom{20}{1}(\tfrac{1}{3})^1(\tfrac{2}{3})^{20-1} = 0.003$$
$$p(2g) = \binom{20}{2}(\tfrac{1}{3})^2(\tfrac{2}{3})^{20-2} = 0.014$$

(correct to three decimal places)

etc.

Continuing in this fashion, the full results are as follows, where x is the number of green beads and $p(x)$ is the probability of achieving this value of x.

x	$p(x)$	x	$p(x)$
0	0.000	11	0.025
1	0.003	12	0.009
2	0.014	13	0.003
3	0.043	14	0.001
4	0.091	15	0.000
5	0.146	16	0.000
6	0.182	17	0.000
7	0.182	18	0.000
8	0.148	19	0.000
9	0.099	20	0.000
10	0.054		

If we now plot the above values on a relative frequency histogram we obtain Figure 12.3 below.

The interesting feature of Figure 12.3 is that although we no longer have any right to expect symmetry (since p and q are no longer equal), it *is* in fact still fairly symmetrical. It is, indeed, a fortunate fact that provided np and nq are

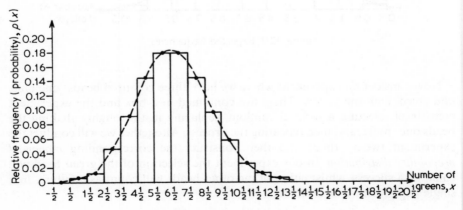

Figure 12.3 The bead experiment (conducted 20 times)

both greater than about 5, the histogram obtained is reasonably symmetrical regardless of the value of p. Further, the outline of these histograms is a reasonable approximation to what we call the *normal probability distribution* curve, enabling us to perform certain calculations which especially for larger values of n, would otherwise be virtually impossible – this topic is discussed further later in the chapter.

12.2 The mean and variance of the binomial probability distribution

It can be shown that, using the standard symbolism, the mean of this distribution is np whilst the variance is npq or $np(1 - p)$. For most purposes, it will be sufficient if these relationships are noted without worrying too much about their derivation. However, for students who require it, formal proofs are supplied in the Appendix.

Example 1 : A tetrahedral die, whose faces are numbered 1 to 4, is thrown 10 times. Find the probability of obtaining (a) no 4s, (b) three 4s, and (c) at least three 4s.

(a) p clearly equals $\frac{1}{4}$.

Now $p(x) = \binom{n}{x}p^x q^{n-x}$; and here $x = 0$, $p = \frac{1}{4}$, $q = 1 - \frac{1}{4} = \frac{3}{4}$, therefore:

$$p(0) = \binom{10}{0}(\tfrac{1}{4})^0(\tfrac{3}{4})^{10-0}$$

$$= 1 \times 1 \times (\tfrac{3}{4})^{10}$$

$$= 0.0563$$

The probability of obtaining no 4s is 0.056.

(b) $$p(3) = \binom{10}{3}(\tfrac{1}{4})^3(\tfrac{3}{4})^7$$

$$= \frac{10 \times 9 \times 8}{3!} \times \tfrac{1}{64} \times \tfrac{2187}{16\,384}$$

$$= 0.250$$

The probability of obtaining three 4s is 0.250.

(c) $$p(\text{at least } 3) = 1 - p(0) - p(1) - p(2)$$

$$p(1) = \binom{10}{1}(\tfrac{1}{4})^1(\tfrac{3}{4})^9$$

$$= 10 \times \tfrac{1}{4} \times (0.75)^9$$

$$= 0.1877$$

$$p(2) = \binom{10}{2}(\tfrac{1}{4})^2(\tfrac{3}{4})^8$$

$$= 45 \times \tfrac{1}{16} \times \tfrac{6561}{65\,536}$$

$$= 0.2816$$

and

$$p(0) = 0.0564 \quad \text{(from part (a))}$$

Thus

$$p(\text{at least } 3) = 1 - 0.0564 - 0.1878 - 0.2816$$

$$= 1.0000 - 0.5257$$

$$= 0.4743$$

The probability of obtaining at least three 4s is 0.474.

Example 2 :   With a certain machine producing washers, the probability of a defective item is 0.01. Calculate the mean and the standard deviation for the distribution of defective washers, when the total number is 500.

We have $n = 500$ and $p = 0.01$, so

$$q = 1 - 0.01$$

$$= 0.99$$

Therefore,

$$\text{Mean} = np$$

$$= 500 \times 0.01$$

$$= 5$$

$$\text{Variance} = npq$$

$$= 500 \times 0.01 \times 0.99$$

$$= 4.95$$

So

$$\text{Standard deviation} = \sqrt{4.95}$$

$$= 2.225$$

N.B.   Since the mean or expected value is 5, the *most likely* result, in a batch of 500 washers is that 5 would be defective.

The mean is 5 and the standard deviation is 2.23.

12.3   The normal distribution for continuous (and discrete) variables

Throughout this book stress has been laid on two facets of statistics: firstly, the importance of the statistical parameters mean and standard deviation, and secondly, the fact that a great many variables, be they continuous or discrete, have frequency distributions that approximate quite closely in outline to a bell-shaped curve known as the *normal distribution curve* or more simply as the '*normal*' curve. (This distribution is often said to be Gaussian, which is somewhat ironic as it appears to have been discovered first by de Moivre in the mid-eighteenth century.)

The reason for this persistence will now be justified! Variables of the type just mentioned are said to be 'normally' distributed and as we shall see their means, μ, and standard deviations, σ, play an important and inseparable part in determining the equations of their various outline curves. Let us now look at these 'normal' curves in more detail.

12.4   Properties of the normal distribution curve

If x is a normally distributed variable having a mean μ and a standard deviation, σ, it can be shown that the equation of the curve outlining its distribution is given by:

$$y = \frac{1}{\sigma\sqrt{2\pi}}\, e^{-(x-\mu)^2/2\sigma^2}$$

This bell-shaped curve is plotted in Figure 12.4, and the following points should be noted:

(a)   the curve is symmetrical about the mean, μ,
(b) x can range in value from $-\infty$ to $+\infty$,
(c)   the total area under the curve is 1,
(d)   the curve never touches the x-axis,
(e)   the maximum value of y is approximately 0.4/standard deviation or $0.4/\sigma$.

Now unlike the binomial distribution for a *discrete* variable, where we *could* talk about the probability of x equalling an individual value such as 3, say, with a normal distribution for a *continuous* variable we can only talk about the probability of x lying within a certain range. For example, the probability that x lies within the range $a \to b$ will equal the *area* beneath the curve in Figure 12.4 lying between the ordinates $x = a$ and $x = b$ (the shaded area on the diagram).

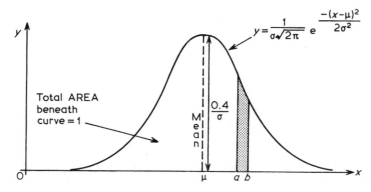

Figure 12.4 A typical normal distribution curve

or,

$$p(a < x < b) = \int_a^b \frac{1}{\sigma\sqrt{2\pi}} e^{-(x-\mu)^2/2\sigma^2} dx$$

It can also be shown that by the time we have gone three standard deviations either side of the mean we will have covered more than 99.7 per cent of the area beneath the curve, as shown in Figure 12.5.

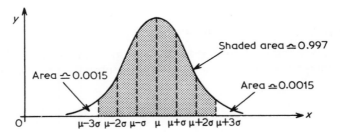

Figure 12.5

In fact, the area between $\mu - \sigma$ and $\mu + \sigma = 0.6827$; the area between $\mu - 2\sigma$ and $\mu + 2\sigma = 0.9545$, and the area between $\mu - 3\sigma$ and $\mu + 3\sigma = 0.9973$. Thus, we can be more than 95 per cent certain that a normally-distributed variable will lie somewhere within two standard deviations of its mean value. The reader can now appreciate why the mean and the standard deviation are such important quantities in statistics.

12.5   Standardization of the normal distribution curve

The equation of the 'normal' curve is complicated and it is obviously desirable to simplify it if we can. Fortunately this is possible and, provided our distribution *is* normal, we can *standardize* it in the following way. We replace our original variable x by a new *standardized* variable z, where

$$z = \frac{x - \mu}{\sigma}.$$

The equation

$$y = \frac{1}{\sigma\sqrt{2\pi}} e^{-(x-\mu)^2/2\sigma^2}$$

then reduces to

$$y = \frac{1}{\sqrt{2\pi}} e^{-z^2/2}$$

This curve (see Figure 12.6) still has the same basic shape but is now symmetrical about the y-axis, so that its mean is 0. Further, it can be shown that its standard deviation is 1.

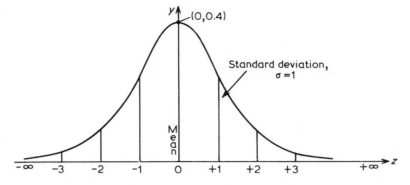

Figure 12.6 Standardized normal curve

N.B. (a) z, like x, still ranges from $-\infty$ to $+\infty$.
(b)   The total area under the curve still equals 1.
(c)   The y co-ordinate at the origin, where the curve reaches its peak, is now about 0.4 ($0.4/\sigma = 0.4/1 = 0.4$).
(d) $p(-1 < z < 1)$ still equals 0.6827
       $p(-2 < z < 2)$ still equals 0.9545
       $p(-3 < z < 3)$ still equals 0.9973
The utility of the standardized normal curve will now be discussed.

12.6   Applications of the standardized normal curve

We have already mentioned that for the 'normal' curve the probability that z lies between -1 and $+1$ is 0.6827. This latter value represents the proportion of the total area under the curve lying between the ordinates -1 and 1, i.e. the shaded area in Figure 12.7.

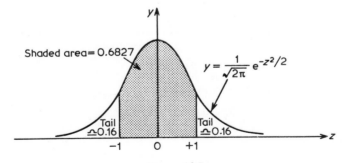

Figure 12.7

Fortunately, we do not need to keep on evaluating the integral of $\dfrac{1}{\sqrt{2\pi}}e^{-z^2/2}$

between appropriate limits in order to find such areas. Tables of these integrals have been compiled and, due to the symmetry of the curve, usually take the following form: values of z are listed, running from 0 upwards, and opposite

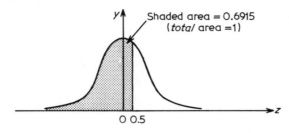

Figure 12.8

each an area is given, which is the area under the curve between $-\infty$ and z. For example, if we look up the value corresponding to $z = 0.5$ in a set of these tables, we find a figure of 0.6915. This means that the shaded area (shown in Figure 12.8 is 0.6915.

Now, suppose we require $p(-1 < z < +1)$. We can use the tables to find this probability as follows: by symmetry the area between -1 and $+1$ equals *twice* the area between 0 and 1. For $z = 0$, of course, we find a value of 0.5000; for $z = 1$ we find a value of 0.8413; so the area between 0 and $1 = 0.8413 - 0.5000 = 0.3413$. Therefore, the required probability is $2 \times 0.3413 = 0.6826$, i.e.

$p(-1 < z < +1) = 0.6826$, which, when corrected, is the value we gave before.

One further example: suppose we require the probability that z lies between -0.5 and $+2$ (the shaded area in Figure 12.9).

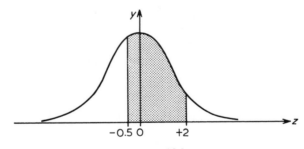

Figure 12.9

Using the tables on pages 236 and 237:

$$p(0 < z < 2) = 0.9772 - 0.5000$$

$$= 0.4772$$

$$p(-0.5 < z < 0) = p(0 < z < 0.5) \text{ (by symmetry)}$$

$$= 0.6915 - 0.5000$$

$$= 0.1915$$

Therefore,

$$p(-0.5 < z < 2) = p(-0.5 < z < 0) + p(0 < z < 2)$$

$$= 0.1915 + 0.4772$$
$$= 0.6687$$

The probability that z lies between -0.5 and 2 is 0.6687.

12.7   Examples

[Examples 3 and 4 can be omitted if desired.]

Example 1:   The mean height of 1000 adults was found to be 175 cm with a standard deviation of 20 cm. Assuming the heights are normally distributed estimate (a) the number of adults who have heights between 135 and 160 cm and (b) the number of adults who have heights greater than 200 cm.

(a)   We have $\mu = 175$ and $\sigma = 20$. Now $z = \dfrac{x - \mu}{\sigma}$, so here

$$z = \frac{x - 175}{20};$$

When $x = 135$,

$$z = \frac{135 - 175}{20} = -2$$

When $x = 160$,

$$z = \frac{160 - 175}{20} = -0.75$$

So we require $p(-2 < z < -0.75)$ which, by symmetry, is equal to

$$p(0.75 < z < 2) = 0.9772 - 0.7734$$
$$= 0.2038$$

Therefore, the number of adults involved

$$1000 \times 0.2038 = 203.8$$

The number of adults having heights between 135.0 and 160 cm is approximately 204.

(b) when $x = 200$,

$$z = \frac{200 - 175}{20} = 1.25$$

$$p(z > 1.25) = 1 - p(z < 1.25)$$
$$= 1.0000 - 0.8944$$
$$= 0.1056$$

So the number of adults involved is

$$1000 \times 0.1056 = 105.6$$

The number of adults who have heights greater than 200 cm is approximately 106.

The above example dealt with a continuous variable (height). However, we can still make use of the normal curve, even if we are dealing with a discrete variable such as an examination mark, *provided we make certain assumptions*. Let us illustrate this by means of another example.

Example 2:   500 candidates took an examination and their mean mark was found to be 61.3 with a standard deviation of 9.8. Estimate (a) the number of candidates who obtained a mark of 67, (b) the number of candidates who obtained between 65 and 74 marks inclusive, and (c) the pass mark if it is desired that only 40 per cent of the candidates should succeed.

(a)   The integer 67 would be assigned to any value in the range 66.5 to 67.5, so, we require $p(66.5 < x < 67.5)$.

Here $\bar{x} = 61.3$ and $\sigma = 9.8$. Now $z = \dfrac{x - \mu}{\sigma}$, so when $x = 66.5$,

$$z = \frac{66.5 - 61.3}{9.8}$$

$$= 0.53$$

When $x = 67.5$,

$$z = \frac{67.5 - 61.3}{9.8}$$

$$= 0.63$$

$$p(0.53 < z < 0.63) = 0.7357 - 0.7019$$

$$= 0.0338$$

Therefore the number of candidates involved is

$$500 \times 0.0338 = 16.9$$

$$= 17 \text{ to the nearest whole number}$$

The number of candidates obtaining a mark of 67 is about 17.

(b)   65–74 inclusive will cover all values in the range 64.5 − 74.5.
When $x = 64.5$,

$$z = \frac{64.5 - 61.3}{9.8}$$

$$= 0.33$$

When $x = 74.5$,

$$z = \frac{74.5 - 61.3}{9.8}$$

$$= 1.35$$

$$p(0.33 < z < 1.35) = 0.9115 - 0.6293$$

$$= 0.2822$$

So the number of candidates involved is

$$500 \times 0.2822 = 141.1$$

$$= 141 \text{ to the nearest whole number}$$

The number of candidates obtaining between 65 and 74 marks is about 141.

(c)   Let the pass mark be X, therefore

$$z = \frac{X - 61.3}{9.8} = z' \text{ (say)}$$

Now we require that $p(z < z') = 0.6$, and from the tables $z' = 0.253$, so

$$\frac{X - 61.3}{9.8} = 0.253$$

$$\Rightarrow X - 61.3 = 2.48$$

$$\Rightarrow X \qquad = 63.78$$

$$= 64 \text{ to the nearest whole number.}$$

The pass mark, if only 40 per cent of the candidates are to be successful,

should be about 64.

Example 3:   Discs produced by a machine are required to have a thickness of between 1.99 and 2.01 mm. Of all the discs produced 7 per cent are rejected as being too thin and 4 per cent are rejected as being too thick. Assuming the thicknesses to be normally distributed with a mean of μ and a standard deviation of σ, form two simultaneous equations in μ and σ and hence evaluate each of these quantities, correct to three significant figures.

When $x = 1.99$,

$$z = \frac{1.99 - \mu}{\sigma}$$

Using the tables for the normal distribution, if 7 per cent of the area under the curve is to lie to the *left* of z, then $z = -1.48$, so

$$-1.48 = \frac{1.99 - \mu}{\sigma} \tag{1}$$

When $x = 2.01$,

$$z = \frac{2.01 - \mu}{\sigma}$$

If 96 per cent (100–4) of the area under the curve is to lie to the left of z, then this time $z = 1.75$, so

$$1.75 = \frac{2.01 - \mu}{\sigma} \tag{2}$$

From equation (2)

$$1.75\sigma = 2.01 - \mu$$

From equation (1)

Subtracting:
$$\frac{-1.48\sigma = 1.99 - \mu}{3.23\sigma = 0.02}$$

Therefore

$$\sigma = \frac{0.02}{3.23}$$

$$= 0.006\ 192$$

Substituting for σ in equation (2)

$$1.75 \times 0.006\ 193 = 2.01 - \mu$$

$$0.010\ 84 = 2.01 - \mu$$

$$\Rightarrow \mu = 1.999\ 16$$

The mean is 2.00 mm and the standard deviation is 0.006 19 mm

(correct to three significant figures).

Example 4:   Two variables are both normally distributed. One variable has a mean of 15 and a standard deviation of 2, whilst the other has a mean of 15 and a standard deviation of 6. Sketch the normal probability distribution curves for each of these variables on the same diagram.

The equation associated with a variable, normally distributed with a mean of μ and a standard deviation of σ, is:

$$y = \frac{1}{\sigma\sqrt{2\pi}} e^{-(x-\mu)^2/2\sigma^2}$$

So when $x = \mu$

$$y = \frac{1}{\sigma\sqrt{2\pi}}e^0$$

$$= \frac{1}{\sigma\sqrt{2\pi}}$$

i.e. at the peak of the curve the y co-ordinate will be

$$\frac{1}{\sigma\sqrt{2\pi}} \simeq \frac{0.4}{\sigma}$$

Also, over 99 per cent of the area under the curve will lie between $\mu - 3\sigma$ and $\mu + 3\sigma$.

For the variable with $\mu = 15$ and $\sigma = 2$

$$\frac{0.4}{\sigma} = \frac{0.4}{2}$$

$$= 0.2$$

$$\mu - 3\sigma = 15 - 6$$

$$= 9$$

and

$$\mu + 3\sigma = 15 + 6$$

$$= 21$$

Similarly for the other variable with $\bar{x} = 15$ and $\sigma = 6$,

$$\frac{0.4}{6} = \frac{0.4}{6} \simeq 0.07$$

$$\mu - 3\sigma = 15 - 18 = -3$$

$$\mu + 3\sigma = 15 + 18$$

$$= 33$$

Therefore, sketches of the two curves will be as shown in Figure 12.10.

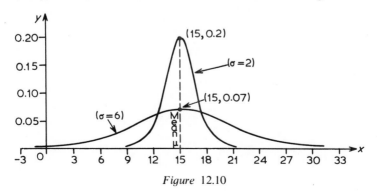

Figure 12.10

12.8   The approximation of the binomial distribution to the normal distribution

We have already mentioned in Section 12.1 that, when considering an experiment involving n trials where the probability of success in an individual experiment is p and that of failure is q, it is tedious to have to apply the binomial probability distribution for large values of n. Moreover, provided np and nq are both greater than about 5, the normal distribution becomes a good approximation to the binomial. Let us demonstrate this by means of a simple example.

Example: A perfectly fair conventional die is thrown 40 times. (a) Use the bionomial probability distribution to find the probability that exactly three sixes are obtained. (b) Show that the normal distribution gives a good approximation.

(a)   We have $n = 40$, $p = \frac{1}{6}$, $q = \frac{5}{6}$, and $x = 3$.

$$p(3) = \binom{40}{3}(\tfrac{1}{6})^3(\tfrac{5}{6})^{37}$$

$$= 0.053\ 78$$

The probability of obtaining three sixes is 0.054 (correct to two

significant figures).

N.B. $(\frac{5}{6})^{37}$ is not the kind of expression one would wish to come across too frequently!

(b) $n = 40$, $p = \frac{1}{6}$, and $q = \frac{5}{6}$, so both np and nq are greater than 5. Therefore the normal distribution should be a good approximation.

The integer 3 covers all values from $2.5 \rightarrow 3.5$, so we require $p(2.5 < x < 3.5)$.

Now, $z = \dfrac{x - \mu}{\sigma}$, and for the binomial distribution, μ is np, so

$$\mu = 40 \times \tfrac{1}{6}$$

$$= 6.667$$

and

$$\sigma = \sqrt{npq}$$

$$= \sqrt{40 \times \tfrac{1}{6} \times \tfrac{5}{6}}$$

$$= 2.357$$

So when $x = 2.5$,

$$z = \frac{2.500 - 6.667}{2.357}$$

$$= -1.77;$$

and when $x = 3.5$,

$$z = \frac{3.500 - 6.667}{2.357}$$

$$= -1.34;$$

$$p(-1.77 < z < -1.34) = 0.9616 - 0.9099$$

$$= 0.0517$$

$$= 0.052 \text{ (correct to two significant figures)}$$

The probability of obtaining three sixes is 0.052.

N.B. This result compares favourably with the value obtained in part (a), and was far easier to obtain! In addition, it can be seen from the example that provided np and nq are both greater than about 5 the binomial distribution approximates to a normal distribution of mean np and standard deviation $\sqrt{npq}$ or $\sqrt{np(1-p)}$.

12.9   Confidence intervals

As already mentioned, if a variable x is normally distributed with a mean of μ and a standard deviation of σ, the probability that x takes some value between $\mu - \sigma$ and $\mu + \sigma$ is 0.6827 or 68.27 per cent. The probability that takes some value between $\mu - 2\sigma$ and $\mu + 2\sigma$ is 0.9545 or 95.45 per cent. The probability that it takes some value between $\mu - 3\sigma$ and $\mu + 3\sigma$ is 0.9973 or 99.73 per cent. Referring to a standardized normal distribution, then, we have the following results for the standardized variable z (where $z = (x - \mu)/\sigma$):

$$p(-1 < z < 1) \text{ is } 68.27 \text{ per cent.}$$
$$p(-2 < z < 2) \text{ is } 95.45 \text{ per cent.}$$
$$p(-3 < z < 3) \text{ is } 99.73 \text{ per cent.}$$

When we quote ranges of values for a variable in this way, we are using what are known as percentage *confidence intervals*. Notice how the more certain we want to be that a variable does lie within a particular range, the greater we have to make that range and, of course, we can never be 100 per cent certain, since, theoretically, z can take any value from $-\infty$ to $+\infty$.

All this illustrates the fact that statistics is not always an exact science, and we clearly have to strike a balance between how certain we want to be and how specific we want to be. Now the range $-1 < z < +1$ is clearly *too* specific because we can only be 68.27 per cent certain that z falls within it and this is certainly not certain enough! In practice, then, we generally use the other two confidence intervals mentioned, and for convenience we normally round these off to 95 per cent and 99 per cent. Having done this, of course, we now need to be quite clear just what range of values of z we are covering in each case.

Consider the first confidence interval: 95 per cent. We need to know the value of z', such that $p(-z' < z < +z')$ is 95 per cent, i.e. as shown in Figure 12.11.

From Figure 12.11 we can see that $p(z < z')$ is $100 - 2.5 = 97.5$ per cent or 0.9750. Using a table for the normal distribution function we find that $z' = 1.96$.

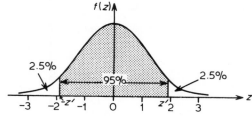

Figure 12.11

In an exactly analogous manner we can show that for the 99 per cent confidence interval $z' = 2.58$.

To summarize our results:

We can be 95 per cent confident that z lies between -1.96 *and* $+1.96$, *and we can be 99 per cent confident that z lies between* -2.58 *and* $+2.58$.

If we are asked to use confidence intervals other than the 95 or 99 per cent then we must make the appropriate calculations, as above, in order to find z'.

Example: The weight of the contents of a '2 kg' packet of frozen food is normally distributed with a mean of 2.05 kg and a standard deviation of 0.015 kg. Estimate 95 and 99 per cent confidence limits for the weight of contents in a single '2 kg' packet.

95 per cent: We require 95 per cent confidence limits, that is to say we require the upper and lower limits for the mean which, we can be 95 per cent certain, will not be transgressed. Here: $\mu = 2.05$ and $\sigma = 0.015$, and we know that we can be 95 per cent confident that $-1.96 < z' < 1.96$;

Now let the upper weight limit be x:

$$z = \frac{x - \mu}{\sigma}$$

So here, therefore,

$$1.96 = \frac{x - 2.05}{0.015}$$

$$\Rightarrow x - 2.05 = 0.0294$$

$$\Rightarrow x = 2.0794 \text{ lb}$$

Let the lower weight limit be x':

$$-1.96 = \frac{x' - 2.05}{0.015}$$

$$\Rightarrow x' - 2.05 = -0.0294$$

$$\Rightarrow x' = 2.0206 \text{ kg},$$

If we round off these values to two decimal places we can then give the answer in two forms:

(1) 95 per cent confidence limits are 2.02 to 2.08 kg;

(2) 95 per cent confidence limits are 2.05 ± 0.03 kg.

99 per cent: It is left to the reader, as a useful exercise, to evaluate these limits. (For the answer see page 209.)

Sometimes, rather than wishing to know the probability that z lies within a particular range *symmetrically* located either side of the mean (0), we may wish to know the probability that z is not smaller than or greater than some particular value. For an example let us calculate a value z' such that:

$$p(z < z') = 0.95$$

Diagrammatically, it will be the shaded area in Figure 12.12.

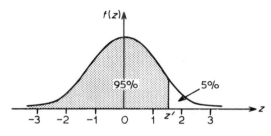

Figure 12.12

From tables of the normal distribution function, z' turns out to lie half way between 1.64 and 1.65, i.e. $z' = 1.645$. Similarly, if we want to be 95 per cent confident that z is *not less* than a particular value then, by symmetry, this equals *minus* 1.645. In a precisely analogous manner we can show that for a 99 per cent confidence interval $z' = 2.33$ (or -2.33).

To summarize these results:

We can be 95 percent confident that z is not greater than 1.645 (or less than -1.645),

and we can be 99 per cent confident that z is not greater than 2.33 (or less than -2.33).

Notice once again, that the more certain we wish to be the less specific we can be.

12.10   Samples taken from a large population

Suppose we take a number of samples, each of size n, from a large population having a mean μ and a standard deviation σ, then it has been found that:
(1) the mean of the sample-means approximates closely to μ (the mean of the parent population)
(2) the standard deviation of the sample-means, sometimes called the *standard error of the mean*, approximates closely to $\sigma/\sqrt{n}$.

N.B. These results hold good whether the samples are large or small or *whether the population is normally distributed or not.*

We normally specify a large population in order that it remains virtually unchanged even after a number of samples have been removed. However, if we sample 'with replacement', that is to say each time we select a member of our sample we return it to the population before selecting the next, then the population need not even be large.

To illustrate the truth of these postulates let us consider a very small population comprising the numbers 1, 4, 5, 7, 10, and 12. Let us now select, with replacement, all the possible sample pairs:

1	1	4	1	5	1	7	1	10	1	12	1
1	4	4	4	5	4	7	4	10	4	12	4
1	5	4	5	5	5	7	5	10	5	12	5
1	7	4	7	5	7	7	7	10	7	12	7
1	10	4	10	5	10	7	10	10	10	12	10
1	12	4	12	5	12	7	12	10	12	12	12

(*N.B.* $n = 2$)

The means of each of these samples will be:

1.0	2.5	3.0	4.0	5.5	6.5
2.5	4.0	4.5	5.5	7.0	8.0
3.0	4.5	5.0	6.0	7.5	8.5
4.0	5.5	6.0	7.0	8.5	9.5
5.5	7.0	7.5	8.5	10.0	11.0
6.5	8.0	8.5	9.5	11.0	12.0

and the mean of these mean values is 6.5. The mean of the population is also 6.5 – so this vindicates the first postulate.

The standard deviation of these mean values is 2.605 (using Four-Figure Tables), and for the population, the standard deviation σ is 3.685. Hence

$$\sigma/\sqrt{n} = 3.685/\sqrt{2}$$

$$= 3.685 \div 1.414$$

$$= 2.605$$

Thus the second postulate is vindicated.

12.11   Distribution of sample means – the central limit theorem

If we take a number of large samples ($n > 25$, say) from a population having a mean μ and a standard deviation σ, then *irrespective of whether this population is normally distributed or not*, the sample-means will approximate to a normal distribution having a mean μ and a standard deviation $\sigma/\sqrt{n}$. This important theorem, by Pierre Simon Laplace (1749–1827), is known as the *central limit theorem*. If the *population* is normally distributed, then the above holds true for *small* samples also ($n < \approx 25$).

Before going on to give some examples, it should be mentioned that there is a convention (which some examining bodies completely disregard) which assigns small roman letters to sample parameters (e.g. mean, and standard deviation), and small greek letters to the corresponding population parameters.

Parameter	Sample	Population
Number of members	n	N
Mean	$\bar{x}$	μ
Standard deviation	s	σ

Example 1:   10 000 female students have a mean weight of 63 kg with a standard deviation of 7 kg. 100 samples of size 36 are taken, without replacement, from the above. Estimate (a) the mean and standard deviation of the sample-means and (b) the proportion of sample-means lying between 60 and 65 kg.

(a)   Since the population is comparatively large, we can use the expression $\sigma/\sqrt{n}$ without modification, despite taking samples without replacement.

For the population: $\mu = 63$ and $\sigma = 7$.
For the sample   : $n = 36$.
Therefore, the mean of the sample-means should equal $\mu (= 63)$ and the standard deviation of the sample-means should equal $\dfrac{\sigma}{\sqrt{n}}\left(= \dfrac{7}{\sqrt{36}} = 1.17 \right).$

The mean should be 63. The standard deviation should be 1.17.

(b) Since we are dealing with large samples ($n > 25$) we can assume that the sample-means are normally distributed with a mean of 63 and a standard deviation of 1.17.

We require $p(60 < \text{sample-mean} < 65)$, so standardizing:

$$z = \frac{x\text{-mean}}{\text{standard deviation}}$$

When $x = 60$:

$$z = \frac{60 - 63}{1.17}$$

$$= -2.56$$

When $x = 65$:

$$z = \frac{65 - 63}{1.17}$$

$$= 1.71$$

i.e. we require $p(-2.56 < z < 1.71) = 0.9512$.
About 95 per cent of the sample-means should lie between 60 and 65 kg.

Example 2:   In a particular examination the mean mark of all candidates in the U.K. was found to be 52, with a standard deviation of 12 marks, these marks being normally distributed. In a particular school 49 pupils took this exam and their mean mark was found to be 57. Is there anything to suggest that the pupils in this school are significantly better than the country as a whole?

For the population : $\mu = 52, \sigma = 12$
For the sample   : $n = 49$
So, the sample-means should be normally distributed with a mean of 52 and a standard deviation of

$$\frac{12}{\sqrt{49}} \simeq 1.71$$

Now $z = \dfrac{x\text{-mean}}{\text{standard deviation}}$ therefore, when $x = 57$:

$$z = \frac{57 - 52}{1.71}$$

$$\simeq 2.92$$

Since 99 per cent of the 'z' values should lie between $-\infty$ and 2.33, and we have a 'z' value of 2.92. We can be almost certain that the pupils in this school are significantly better than average.

Example 3:   The life-times of a particular car battery are normally distributed with a mean of 48 months and a standard deviation of 8 months. A modified battery is produced and a random sample of 16 are found to have a mean life-time of 52 months. Is there any evidence that the new battery is significantly better at (a) the 5 per cent level and (b) the 1 per cent level?

(a)   'The 5 per cent level' simply means that we want only a 5 per cent chance that any assertion we make is wrong. In other words we want to be 95 per cent certain that we are right. Accordingly, we need to consider 95 per cent confidence limits.

Although the sample is small ($n < 25$), the sample-means should still be approximately normally distributed since the population from which they come is normally distributed.

For the population : $\mu = 48, \sigma = 8$
For the sample   : $n = 16, \bar{x} = 52$
The mean of the sample-means should be $\mu = 48$.

The standard deviation of the sample-means should be $\dfrac{\sigma}{\sqrt{n}} = \dfrac{8}{\sqrt{16}} = 2$;

Now $z = \dfrac{x\text{-mean}}{\text{standard deviation}}$, and when $x = 52$: ⁃

$$z = \frac{52 - 48}{2}$$

$$= 2.00$$

Now, we can be 95 per cent confident that z is less than 1.645, and since our value of z is greater than this, we can assert that there is a significant improvement (at the 5 per cent level).

(b) 'The 1 per cent level' means that we require 99 per cent confidence limits. Now, we can be 99 per cent confident that z is less than 2.33, and since our value of z is *less* than this, we can now assert that there is no improvement (at the 1 per cent level).

A qualitative summary of these results would be that the new batteries are probably better.

12.12   One-tailed and two-tailed significance tests

When we are merely interested in knowing the probability that our standardized variable z is not greater than (or less than) some particular value, we are said to be performing a 'one-tailed' test. For example, we have already shown that $p(-\infty < z < 1.645) = 0.95$, and the area of uncertainty (0.05 or 5 per cent) is wholly concentrated in a right-hand tail, as shown in Figure 12.13.

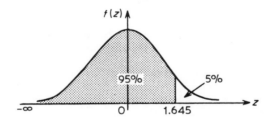

Figure 12.13 One-tailed test at the 5 per cent level

If, however, we wish to know the probability that z lies within a particular range symmetrically located either side of the mean 0, we are said to be performing a 'two-tailed' test. For example we have previously shown that $p(-2.58 < z < 2.58) = 0.99$, and the area of uncertainty (0.01 or 1 per cent) is now concentrated into *two* tails (a left-hand and a right-hand tail) each having an area of $\frac{1}{2}$ per cent, as shown in Figure 12.14.

Generally, the *context* of a particular problem will make it apparent whether a one- or two-tailed test is required. However, this is a complex topic which can only be touched upon here, and students who are interested will clearly need to consult more advanced works.

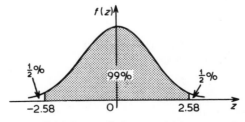

Figure 12.14 Two-tailed test at the 1 per cent level

Exercise 12

1. Because of a fault in a machine, 10 per cent of the articles it produces are defective. If a random sample of 6 articles produced by the machine is taken, find the probability that no more than one of the articles in the sample is defective.

    (L.U.)

2. The distribution of boys and girls in 320 families, each with six children, is to be investigated. Assuming that a child is as likely to be a boy as a girl, calculate how many families you would expect to find with (a) no boys, (b) one boy, (c) two boys, and (d) more than three boys.

    (L.U.)

3. As the result of a survey it was decided that the probability of a housewife using a particular furniture polish is 0.1. If five housewives are selected at random, calculate the probability that (a) all of them use this particular polish and (b) exactly two of them use this polish.

    (L.U.)

4. In a consignment of 20 articles just 4 are defective. If a sample of 5 articles is taken at random from this consignment, find the probability that it will contain (a) no defective articles and (b) 3 or more defective articles.

    (O. & C.)

5. In a mating designed to produce brown mice, half of the offspring are expected to be brown. Independently of their colour, the offspring are equally likely to be male or female.
    (a) In a litter of 5 offspring what is the probability of obtaining at least two brown females?
    (b) If several similar pairs of mice are breeding, find the average number of brown females expected among 200 offspring.
    (c) Find also the standard deviation of the number of brown females.

    (O. & C.)

6. On a certain stretch of shingle beach, analysis shows that on average one pebble in ten is of quartz. A random sample of five pebbles is taken from this beach. Calculate the probability of finding in this sample (a) no quartz, (b) exactly 2 quartz, and (c) more than two quartz pebbles.

    (C.U.)

7. The table below shows the relative frequency distribution of the number of seeds in a pod for a certain plant.

Number of seeds per pod	4	5	6	7
Relative frequency	0.20	0.54	0.15	0.11

    If a pod is selected at random, calculate the expected value of the number of seeds in the pod.

    (L.U.)

8. (a) A variable X can take any of the values $1, 2, 3, 4,$ or 5 and the probability of any particular value of X is given by

    $$p(X) = \frac{6X - X^2 - 3}{20}$$

    Calculated the expected value of X.

(b) The probabilities of a particular inoperative piece of equipment having 1, 2, 3, 4 or 5 faulty components are $\frac{1}{3}, \frac{4}{15}, \frac{1}{5}, \frac{2}{15}$, and $\frac{1}{15}$ respectively. Calculate the expected value of the number of faulty components.

(c) Discuss the meaning of *expected value*, illustrating your answer by reference to parts (a) and (b) above.

(L.U.)

9. The table below gives the probabilities of a random variable x for the output of the six plants of the Bach Industries:

Plants	Output, x	Probability
M	1	0.10
N	2	0.25
O	3	0.30
P	4	0.20
Q	5	0.10
R	6	0.05

What is the expected value of X?
A. 2.50.
B. 2.75.
C. 3.10.
D. 3.25.
E. 3.55.

(W.A.E.C.)

10. From prolonged observation on weekdays, during the day, at the ticket office of a main line terminus the probabilities of finding 0, 1, 2, 3, 4, and 5 people waiting were stated to be 0.08, 0.17, 0.31, 0.28, 0.14, and 0.02 respectively. Calculate (a) the expected value and (b) the variance of the number of people waiting.

(L.U.)

11. A variable Y is normally distributed with a mean of 70 and a standard deviation of 12. Calculate
(a) the standard score corresponding to $Y = 94$,
(b) the value of Y corresponding to a standard score of -1.5,
(c) the percentage of the population with standard score of zero or greater,
(d) the probability of a value of Y greater than or equal to 94.

(S.C.E.)

12. The marks obtained by 1000 candidates in an examination were normally distributed with a mean of 55 and a standard deviation of 8.
(a) If a mark of 71 or more is required for an A-pass, estimate the number of A-passes awarded.
(b) If 15 per cent of the candidates failed the examination, estimate the minimum mark required for a pass.
(c) Calculate the probability that, of two candidates chosen at random, both passed the examination.

(S.C.E.)

13. Give a rough sketch of a normal probability curve.
(a) Explain what is meant by the term *unit or standardized normal variable*.
(b) Find, using tables, the proportions of the total area under this curve that are within one, two, and three standard deviations respectively of the arithmetic mean.

(c) 200 results are obtained from an experiment and their mean and standard deviation are found to be 5.3 and 0.6 respectively. Assuming that the results are normally distributed, calculate, using tables, how many of them may be expected to be (i) greater than 5.5, (ii) between 4.8 and 4.9.

(L.U.)

14. A certain type of electric light bulb has a burning life of H hours, where H has a normal distribution with mean 1300 hours and standard deviation 125 hours.
(a) What is the probability that a bulb selected at random will burn for more than 1500 hours?
(b) If the manufacturer guarantees to replace any bulb which burns for less than 1050 hours, what percentage of the bulbs will have to be replaced?
(c) If two bulbs are installed at the same time, what is the probability that both will burn for less than 1400 hours but more than 1200 hours?

(N.I.)

15. A cutting machine produces rods which are acceptable if their lengths are between 90 cm and 90.6 cm. Of all the rods produced 5 per cent are rejected as too short and 8 per cent are rejected as too long. Assuming that the lengths of the rods are normally distributed, show that the mean and standard deviation of this distribution are respectively 90.3 cm and 0.197 cm, correct to three significant figures. If the minimum acceptable length is reduced to 89.9 cm find the percentage of the rods that would now be rejected as too short.

(L.U.)

16. (a) Sketch on the same diagram the normal probability curves for two random variables, one having a mean of 10 and a standard deviation of 2, and the other having a mean of 20 and a standard deviation of 4.
(b) A random variable is normally distributed about a mean of 10 with a variance of 4. Use tables to find the probability that its value x is such that $9 \leq x \leq 12$.
(c) Another random variable is normally distributed about a mean of 20 with a variance of 16. The probability that its value y satisfies $18 \leq y \leq k$ is 0.5. Use tables to find the value of k.

(L.U.)

17. Rods are mass produced by a machine. The specification requires the length of each rod to be between 1.49 cm and 1.51 cm. The machine produces rods whose lengths are normally distributed with standard deviation 0.004 cm about a mean which can be set to any desired value. Find the percentage of rods produced which have to be rejected if the machine is set so that the mean length of the rods is (a) 1.500 cm and (b) 1.502 cm.
   Calculate to what mean length the machine must be set so that only about 1 rod in 10 000 will be of length less than 1.49 cm.

(C.U.)

18. The heights of boys in a certain school are normally distributed. 10 per cent are over 1.8 metres and 20 per cent are below 1.6 metres. Use the table of the normal probability integral to form simultaneous equations for the mean height μ metres and the standard deviation σ metres.
Find μ and σ.
Hence find the interquartile range.

(L.U.)

19. A number of bulbs were planted. Assuming that 4 out of every 5 produce a flower, calculate the probability of (a) two flowers, if two bulbs were planted and (b) exactly two flowers, if three bulbs were planted.

Calculate also the approximate probability of obtaining more that 88 flowers, if 100 bulbs were planted, given that for a binomial distribution, the mean $= np$, and the variance $= np(1 - p)$.

(L.U.)

20. A bag contains four green balls and one red ball, which are identical apart from colour. A *trial* consists of making a random selection of a ball from the bag, noting its colour and then returning it to the bag. A *success* consists of drawing the red ball.
(a) Calculate the probability of at least two successes in five trials.
(b) If the trial is repeated 100 times, it may be assumed that the distribution of successes obtained approximates to a normal probability distribution. Calculate the approximate value of the probability of drawing the red ball at least thirty times.

(L.U.)

21. Of the 400 people who make provisional reservations for a holiday tour, previous experience shows that 80 per cent will confirm their reservations. Assuming these people act independently of each other,
(a) calculate the mean and the standard deviation of the number of confirmations expected;
(b) find also the probability that, of the first 6 reservations, at least 3 will subsequently be cancelled.

(O. & C.)

22. An experiment consists of drawing a disc from a bag containing five discs labelled A, B, C, D or E and then replacing it. What is the probability that A will not be chosen?
The bag is then thoroughly shaken before another draw is made. Calculate, using the tables where necessary, the approximate probability of obtaining the disc A at least (a) 2050 times when the experiment is performed 10 000 times, (b) 180 but not more than 190 times when the experiment is performed 900 times.
(You may use the fact that if the probability of choosing the disc A in one experiment is p then, when the experiment is performed n times, the mean and the variance of the probability distribution will be np and $np(1 - p)$ respectively.)

(L.U.)

23. The probability that a child is left-handed is 0.16.
(a) Calculate the mean and standard deviation of the number of left-handed children in a random sample of 100 children.
(b) Taking the distribution of left-hand children in the sample as approximately normal, calculate the probability that a random sample of 100 children contains fewer than 24 left-handed children.

(S.C.E.)

24. Explain briefly what is meant by the standard error of the mean.
A liquid product is manufactured in a series of separate batches each weighing 1 kg. The percentage of acid (by weight) in each batch has a normal distribution with a mean of 2.4 and a standard deviation of 0.25.
(a) Find 95 per cent confidence limits for the percentage of acid in a 1 kg. batch.
(b) If five 1 kg batches are thoroughly mixed together to make a large, 5 kg batch, find 95 per cent confidence limits for the percentage of acid in the mixture.

(O. & C.)

25. Random simple samples of size n are drawn from a population, x, whose mean and variance are μ and σ^2 respectively. If m is the arithmetic mean of the sample, write down the mean and the variance of the distribution of m.
A single random observation drawn from a distribution with given mean and

standard deviation is said to be 'rare' if it differs from the mean by more than 2 standard deviations.

The 2500 pupils at a school are found to have a mean I.Q. of 101. It is known that the I.Q.s of all pupils in the country are distributed normally about a mean of 100 with standard deviation 15. Is there anything to suggest that this is a rare school?

The mean I.Q. of a sample containing n pupils was found to be 100 to the nearest integer. If this sample was not regarded as rare, calculate the maximum value of n.

(C.U.)

26. The diameters of 100 rods, measured in mm to the nearest mm, are classified in the following frequency table:

Diameters in mm	62–64	65–67	68–70	71–73	74–76	77–79
Class frequency	6	14	31	25	17	7

Total 100

Taking the class marks to be 63, 66, ... , etc. show that the mean and the standard deviation of this population are respectively 70.62 and 3.85 mm approximately.

Using the same class marks allocate sampling numbers from 00 to 99 to these data. By reading consecutive pairs of digits from left to right along the following four rows of random numbers select 10 samples each of 4 items.

50 532	25 496	95 652	42 457
73 547	07 136	40 876	79 971
54 195	25 708	27 989	64 728
10 744	08 396	56 242	85 184

Calculate the mean and the standard deviation of the distribution of sample means so determined and compare them with the theoretical values expected for a large number of samples. Comment on the result.

(A.E.B.)

27. The weight of soap powder in a standard packet is normally distributed with a mean of 805.8 grams and a standard deviation of 2.11 grams. Random samples of 16 packets are selected.
(a) Calculate the mean and standard deviation of the mean weight of soap powder per packet in a random sample of 16 packets.
(b) Estimate the weights between which the central 95 per cent of the mean weights per packet in such random samples will lie.

(S.C.E.)

28. When patients suffering from a disease are given a certain treatment the probability of a cure is 0.25.
(a) If this treatment is given to a random sample of 36 patients suffering from the disease, what is the mean and standard deviation of the number of patients cured?
(b) When a new treatment was given to a random sample of 36 patients, suffering from the same disease, it was found that 14 of the patients were cured. At the 5 per cent level of significance does this suggest that the new treatment is more effective than the first treatment?

(S.C.E.)

29. Examination of a large number of similar packets of seeds revealed that the distribution of the number of seeds per packet was $N(98, 12)$, that is to say normal, arithmetic mean 98, and standard deviation 12. Calculate the probability of a customer receiving a packet containing more than 105 seeds.

Examination of a particular batch of 400 packets of this variety gave an arithmetic mean of 100.00. Did this batch contain significantly more seeds per packet than the production as a whole? Show clearly the mathematical reasoning leading to your answer.

(A.E.B.)

30.   (a) The lifetimes in hours of electric lamp-bulbs produced by a certain factory are $N(500, 20)$, that is to say normally distributed, arithmetic mean 500 and standard deviation 20. Calculate the probability that (i) one bulb selected at random will have a life less than 475 hours, (ii) two bulbs selected at random will both last longer than 490 hours.

(b) The marks awarded in a certain G.C.E. examination had an arithmetic mean of 45 and a standard deviation of 15. One particular school entered 49 candidates, whose marks had the same standard deviation but an arithmetic mean of 50. Were the results of this school's entry significantly different from average?

(A.E.B.)

Answer to problem on page 199: 2.011–2.089 kg

Answers

Exercise 1

1. (a) (i) Does not explain the purpose behind the survey. (ii) Does not thank pupils for completing the form. (iii) The name is probably not required in this particular case. (iv) Does not state how accurately age is to be given. (v) Does not state how accurately height is to be given, nor in what units, nor with or without shoes on.
    (b) The rewritten questionnaire should incorporate the above points.
2. The questions should be readily comprehensible, be unambiguous, be brief, not require specialist knowledge to answer, not be emotively phrased, not try and influence the respondent, not give the respondent an easy option.
    (a) 'What is your age?' – this question would not be truthfully answered in some cases. 'Are you between 20 and 30, 30 and 40, etc.' might be better.
    (b) 'Have you any children?' – much too vague. 'Have you any children, if so what are their ages and sexes?' is the kind of question required.
    (c) 'How much does your husband earn per week?' – this question will probably be resented. It would be better to try and arrive at the above information *indirectly*, by asking a question such as 'How much house-keeping money do you receive each week?' or 'How much do you spend on food each week?'.
    (d) 'Make a list of the tinned foods in your house.' People wont bother! Probably better to ask them to list tinned foods of a certain type, or to list tinned foods they have purchased in the last seven days say.
3. C
4. A
5. B, C
6. D
7. See answer to Question 2.
8. A biased sample arises when not every member of the population from which the sample is taken has an equal chance of being selected.

9. (*One possibility*) The purpose of this questionnaire is to ascertain whether there is sufficient demand for a monthly school newsheet. All information given will be treated as strictly confidential. Thank you for your co-operation.

Please answer the following questions as carefully as you can.

(1) What is your form?

(2) What is your age (in years and months)?

(3) What is your sex?

(4) Are you interested in the idea of a monthly newsheet?

(5) Would you be prepared to write articles for the newsheet?

(6) Would you be prepared to contribute items of interest about yourself or other pupils or ex-pupils?

(7) Would you be prepared to pay 3p for the newsheet?

Please return this form, when completed, to your Form Captain.

Each form should receive the appropriate proportion of questionnaires, i.e. if Form I contains one fifth of the pupils at the school it should receive $100 \times 1/5 = 20$ forms. In addition, in each form, an equal number of questionnaires should go to boys and girls. The aim in other words will be to obtain a quota sample of size 100.

10. See pages 2–5 in Chapter 1.

11. Sample of 150 should have 45 from A, 90 from B, and 15 from C.

12. (*Results obtained by author*)

(a) Random sample gave an average of 10.03.

(b) Systematic sample gave an average of 9.98.

(c) Stratified sample gave an average of 9.98.

(d) Average of all 300 values is 9.99. All three samples only use 25 out of the 300 values, therefore they are bound to give an approximate average only; if they happen to give the exact average it is purely a coincidence.

(e) A systematic sample would be permissible and would be best here simply because it is much quicker to compile than a random sample.

13. (*One possibility*). *Employment Prospects for School Leavers.* The purpose of this survey is to learn more about employment prospects for school leavers in this area.

Accordingly, we should be very grateful if you would complete the above form *six months from the date you leave school* and return it to us in the stamped addressed envelope provided.

Naturally, all information you may care to give will be treated in the strictest confidence.

Thank you for your co-operation.

(1) Please complete the following:

Name (*in full*) ....

Address ....

Age last birthday ....

(2) What type of employment have you been seeking in the past six months? (*Space for completion*)

(3) Have you now obtained a full-time job? Yes/No. (*Delete as applicable*)

(4) If so give (i) the name and address of your employer
(*Space for completion*)

(ii) the date on which you commenced work.
(*Space for completion*)

The Chief Education Officer, Blankshire County Council.

14.   (a) 'How many times, on average, do you eat out each month?'
'Are you satisfied with the restaurants at present in the locality?'
'Do you prefer English or Continental-type food?'
'Please list the following in order of preference: grills, salads, snacks.'
(b) Care should be taken to obtain a sample of reasonable size (e.g. for
a population of 10 000 one would probably need say 200 questionnaires).
The sample should also be representative of the whole locality (this
could be done by taking a systematic sample from the local electoral
register, for example).

16.   (a) Take a random sample of 12 from the whole 600.
(b) Take 3 at random from the first years ($\rightarrow$ 3); 2 at random from the
second, third, and fourth years ($\rightarrow$ 6); and 1 at random from the fifth,
sixth, and seventh years ($\rightarrow$ 3).
(c) Take e.g. 2 boys and 2 girls at random from the first, second, third,
and fourth years taken together ($\rightarrow$ 4); 1 boy and 1 girl at random from
the fifth years ($\rightarrow$ 2); and 3 boys and 3 girls at random from the sixth and
seventh years taken together ($\rightarrow$ 6).

17.   Take 1 girl and 1 boy at random from each of the 15 classes ($\rightarrow$ 30), and
take 5 girls and 5 boys at random from the sixth form ($\rightarrow$ 10).

Exercise 2

1.   (a) 10 (b) 30–40 (c) 40–50
(d)

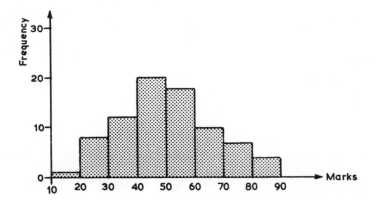

2. (a)

Class	30–31	32–33	34–35	36–37	38–39	40–41	42–43
Frequency	4	6	9	12	10	6	3

(b) 41.5 and 43.5

(c)

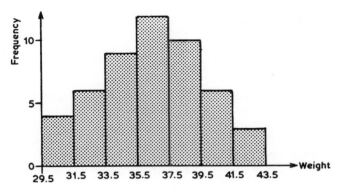

(d) 36–38

3.

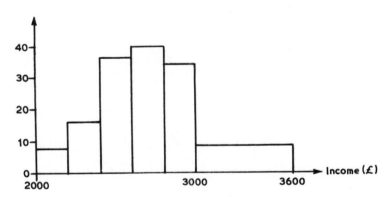

4.

Class	0–2	2–4	4–8	8–16	16–32
Frequency	25	20	30	40	40

5.

Class	0–1	1–3	3–7
Frequency	15	15	20

6. 3

7. 9

8.

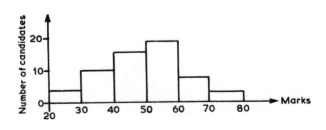

9. *Possible answers* (a) Number of pages, (b) page thickness
10. Continuous, continuous, discrete, continuous, continuous, discrete
11. (a) Discrete
    (b) quantitative
13. A
14. C
15. A
16. D
17.

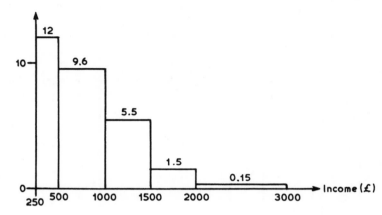

18. (a)

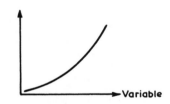

(b)

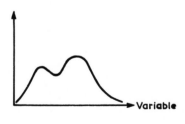

19.

20.

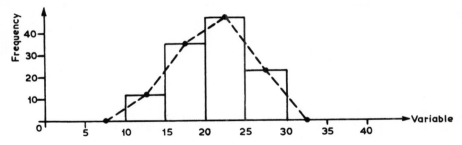

21.

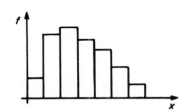

22. Median

23.

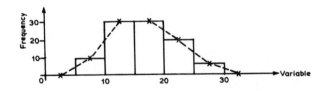

Exercise 3

1. The subject-matter of the table should be clear; the headings should be clear; units should be clearly indicated; totals and sub-totals should be given where appropriate; the table should be kept as simple as possible.

    Male and Female M.P.s in the Labour and Conservative Parties: 1964–1970

Election year	Conservative M F	Labour M F
1964		
1966		
1970		

2. 1.4 : 1
3. It emphasizes the relative proportions of two or more constituents making up a whole.

4. (a) To make the data more readily comprehensible; to emphasize fluctuations in total amounts and/or relative proportions; to encourage people to look at it.

(b) (*One possibility*)

A. A comparative bar chart

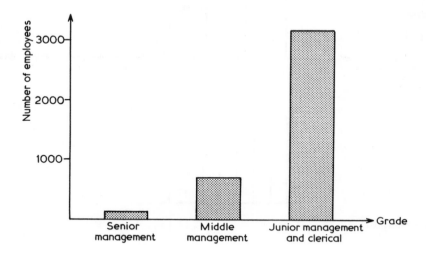

B. A pie-chart

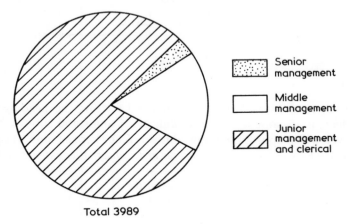

Total 3989

(Approximate sector angles:

Senior management: $11\frac{1}{2}°$

Middle management: $62\frac{1}{2}°$

Junior management and clerical: $286°$

(The sectors could be coloured or shaded and an appropriate key provided)

Bar Chart – advantages: clearly shows the totals in senior, middle, and junior management; not too complicated; disadvantage: not very easy to see the relative number in each grade.

Pie Chart – advantages: easy to see the proportions in each grade; simple and attractive; disadvantage: not easy to see the numbers in each grade.

5. 12 cm

6. $\frac{1}{2}$ unit

7. See answer to Question 4.

8. C

9. (a)

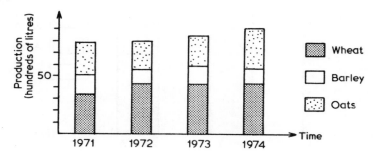

(b)

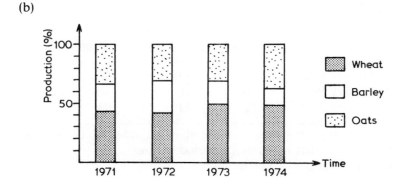

(c) The sectional bar chart shows clearly the variation in *total* production from year to year and also shows reasonably clearly the actual amount of each crop. It does not show the variation in the *relative* amounts of each crop.

The percentage bar chart gives no information on actual production figures. However, it clearly shows the variation in the relative amounts of each crop from year to year.

10. A

11. A : B is as 64 : 1

12. If we are illustrating a number of components making up a whole, an ordinary bar chart will show clearly the numbers of each component, but will not show so clearly the relative amounts, a pie chart, on the other hand, will clearly show the relative amounts, but will not show clearly the actual numbers.

13. Refer to the text on page 34.

14. (a) (i) Bar chart (ii) pie chart (iii) histogram
(b) (*One possibility*)

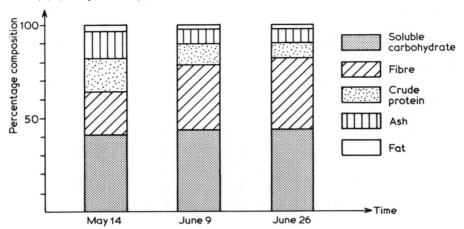

15. (*One possibility*)

| Date | Numbers of Employees | | |
	Men	Women	Total
January 1962	79	11	90
January 1963	76	10	86
January 1964	82	11	93

16. (a) (i) Data comprising a whole, made up of a number of components.
(ii) Similar data that varies over a period of time.
(iii) Grouped Frequency Distributions.
(b) (i)

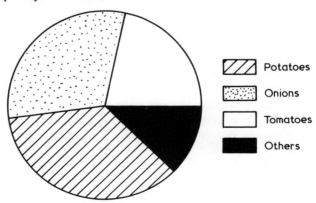

(N.B. Radius is 2 units)

(approximate sector angles: Potatoes: 128.9°, Onions: 109.6°, Tomatoes: 78°, Others: 43.5°)

(ii) 1953: 1.75 units; 1957: 2.02 units

18.   Coal: − 29.7 per cent (E.E.C.) and − 27.1 per cent (U.K.)

Crude Steel: + 50.0 per cent (E.E.C.) and + 15.0 per cent (U.K.)

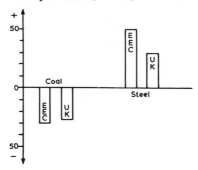

Percentage changes in coal and steel production: 1960/1970

Coal production in the U.K.

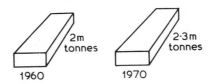

Steel production in the U.K.

19.   *Road Accidents to School Children*

| | Accident | | | Time | | | Distance from zebra crossing | | | Vehicle | | | |
	Slight	Moderate	Severe	A.M.	M.D.	P.M.	0	< 50 m	> 50 m	C	B	L	Total
M													
T	3	—	1	1	1	2	—	2	2	4	—	—	4
W													
Th													
F													

20.

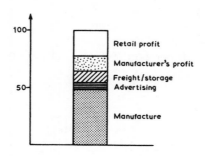

21.

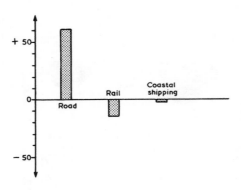

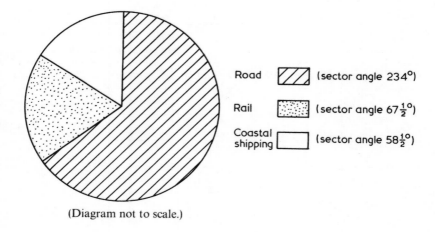

(Diagram not to scale.)

22.

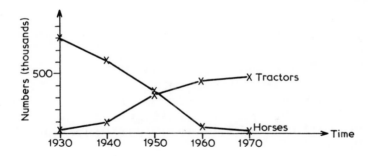

The graph shows that, for all practical purposes, horses had ceased to be used on farms by 1970. The number of tractors in use, after steadily increasing between 1930 and 1960, appeared to be levelling off at about 500 000 in 1970.

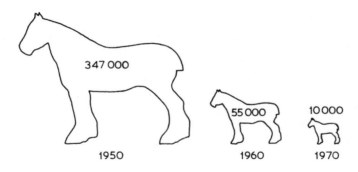

23. *Wales* | Constables 72.6 per cent; Sergeants 17.8 per cent; Inspectors or above 9.6 per cent.
England | Constables 76.5 per cent; Sergeants 15.0 per cent; Inspectors or above 8.5 per cent.

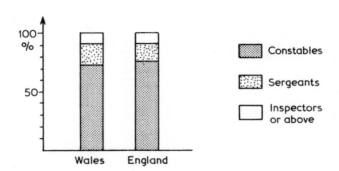

Exercise 4

1. C
2. 95.0, 104.9; (a) 102.0 (b) 8.0 (c) 56.1 per cent
3. 52 per cent
4. (a) 705 (b) 143 (c) 21.9 per cent (d) 6.7 per cent
5. (a) 2.9 (b) 54.8 (c) 63.0 (d) 44.8 per cent
6. (a) £ 2725 (i) £ 2690 (ii) £ 2515 (iii) £ 2905 (iv) 195
7. Median = 42.5 (from polygon) and 43.6 (by calculation)
8. (a) 56, 89, 117, 134, 146, 157, 165, and 170 (b) 47.0 (c) 56.0 (d) 4.82 per cent
9. S.I.R. ≃ 5
10. (a) 61.1 (b) 72 per cent
11. Median (by calculation) = 3.2; S.I.R. (from polygon) = 1.25
12. (a) 5.1 (b) 67.5 per cent
13. (a) 625 (b) 575 and 700 (c) 12; 620 mm
14. (b) Median = 42; quartiles are 18 and 86 (c) 76
15. 53 girls; median (from graph) = 44.7; median (by calculation) = 45.8; 65 points
16. 32 girls (by calculation)
17. (a) 31.8 (b) 18.8 per cent (c) 9.1; assumption is that values are spread evenly across each class
18. 40.5 per cent
19. 67.0 kg
20. A
21. 150 seconds
22.

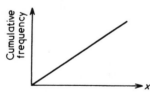

23.

24.

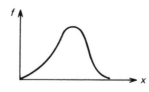

25.

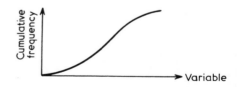

Exercise 5

1. (a) 24.2 (b) 23.5 (c) 23
2. 75
3. 15
4. $(n + 1)/2$

5. 16
6. 25 000
7. D
8. Mean = 10.8; median = 11; mode = 12
9. (a) 6 (b) 6 (c) 4
10. (a) 7 (b) 56 (c) 39
11. (a) 35 (b) 19
12. 13.5; '19.2' is clearly an incorrectly recorded weighing (perhaps for 12.2) and this value will make the mean too large; a better estimate is obtained by ignoring '19.2' and taking the mean of the other six values $\rightarrow$ 12.6.
13. (1) Only a few of the values are used in its compilation. (2) There may be more than one mode.
14. (a) 34.1 (b) 33.2
15. 48.0
16. (a) 55, 65, 75, 85, 95, 110 and 150 (b) 91 (c) $90\frac{5}{6}$
17. D
18. (a) 29.5, 49.5, 69.5, 89.5, 109.5, 129.5, 149.5, 169.5, 189.5, and 229.5 (b) 7, 16, 42, 74, 13, 41, 19, 12, 8, and 8 (c) 106.9
19. (a)

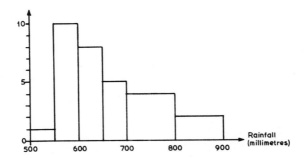

    (b) 644.5 (c) 640
20. Diagrammatically: 7.0; by calculation: 7.0
21. Probably the median (the mean will be distorted by the *large* number of *small* sizes; the mode will be misleading because in this particular distribution the first class is the modal class; median = 21.5).
22. 6
23. 15 years 142 days
24. 1
25. 1.36
26. 8
27. 1
28. Mode = 2; grade of 1
29.

x	16	17	18	19	20	21	22
f	3	7	8	11	12	6	1

Mean = £18.90

Exercise 6

1. 2.33
3. 6.27
4. C
5. D
6. (a) 31 (b) 5.39 (c) 7.65 (d) 58.5
7. 1.3
8. 1
9. (a) 1.4 (b) 14 (c) 5.6
10. (a) 30 (b) 20
11. 48
12. (a) 6 (b) 1.1
13. (a) $\simeq$ 73 (b) 7.9 (c) 33.7 (d) 12.8
14. (a) 13.9 (b) 17.1
15. (a) 29.5, 49.5, 69.5, 89.5, 109.5, 129.5, 149.5, 169.5, 189.5, and 229.5 (b) 7, 16, 42, 74, 73, 41, 19, 12, 8, and 8 (c) 106.9 (d) 38.9
16. Mean = 48, standard deviation = 18.44; overall mean = 50.7, overall standard deviation = 15.92
17. $\frac{4}{3}$
18. 1
19.

x	16	17	18	19	20	21	22
f	3	7	8	11	12	6	1

    (a) 18.90 (b) 1.23 (c) 1.50

20.

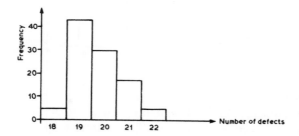

    Standard deviation = 0.97
21. (a)

x	0	1	2	3	4	5
f	14	26	12	6	0	2

    A distribution having positive skew
    (b) Mean = 1.3; standard deviation = 1.13; mean deviation from the mean = 0.87 (c) 5
22. 8
23. 3.6
24. 5

Exercise 7

1. $G = 0.345F + 28$; 45 (b) 0.9
2.

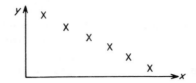

3. 0.29
4. (a) Correlation coefficients: $X = 0.843$; $Y = 0.643$; $Z = 0.871$; $r_{XY} = 0.6$; $r_{XZ} = 0.71$; $r_{YZ} = 0.77$, therefore (a) Z is best judge (b) Y and Z are most in agreement; points of interest: despite the fact that X and Z are much better judges than Y, the correlation between X and Z is in fact worse than that between Y and Z.
   (b)

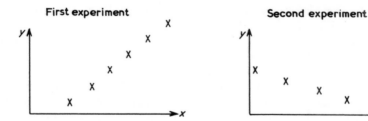

5. 0.77
6. B
7. C
8. 43; $0 = 0.97M$
9. (a) 0

   (b)

Judge	Ranks			
A	1	2	3	4
B	3	1	4	2

10. The slope of the regression line.
11. $a = 1.41$ $b = 2.33$; $y = 15.0$
12. The regression coefficient
13. 0 and 1
14. (a) (i) -1.00 and 1.00
    (ii) 0.00

(b) ranks:

T		12	11	10	$8\frac{1}{2}$	$8\frac{1}{2}$	7	6	5	4	3	2	1
O		11	12	10	9	8	6	6	6	3	4	1	2

0.97

15. $y = 0.2x^2 + 0.5$
16. (a) Replace judge C, since A and B are in good agreement, whereas neither A nor B are in good agreement with C. (b) Yes, replace judge A, since C agrees better with B than with A.
17. (a) 0.94 (c) $\bar{x} = 20.5$, $\bar{y} = 39.75$ (d) $y = 0.44x + 31$ (e) $y = 35.4$
18. (a) -1.0 or $+1.0$ (b) 0; $r = -0.94$; the latter value implies that there is very good negative linear correlation between age and price, i.e. in general terms the greater the age the smaller the price.
19. 0.5
20. (a) 0.94 (c) $\bar{x} = 20.0$, $\bar{y} = 33.0$ (d) $y = 1.5x + 3.0$ (e) 30.0
21. $y = 5$

Exercise 8

1. To make the overall trend more easily discernible; the graph repeats itself every 6 units of time, therefore use 6-point moving averages which are (correct to one decimal place): 4.1, 4.4, 4.6, 4.9, 5.3, 5.6, 6.0, 6.3, 6.6, 7.0, 7.4, 7.7, 8.0, 8.3, 8.6, 8.8, 9.0, 9.3, and 9.6; 10.8
3. 16
4. Graph repeats itself every 6 units of time, therefore use 6-point moving averages which are (correct to the nearest whole number): 167, 168, 168, 171, 171, 173, 173, 174, 174, 180, 181, 180, and 183; 183.5 and 185.0; 254
6. The 4-point moving averages (correct to one decimal place) are: 29.0, 29.8, 31.3, 32.0, 32.5, 32.8, 33.0, 33.0, 33.3, 33.5, 33.8, 34.8, and 35.5. The takings show marked seasonal variation, being high in summer and low in winter; the overall trend is that takings are gradually increasing.
7. 26.4
9. 5-year moving averages are: 45.4, 55.2, 62.4, 73.0, 78.8, 90.6, and 98.8 (lung cancer); 48.8, 40.2, 36.0, 30.0, 26.0, 22.4, and 19.2 (tuberculosis); 136 and 8
10. (a) Four-quarterly moving averages are: 670, 687.5, 705, 725, 745, 765, 790, 810, and 837 (b) 942
11. 49
12. 3.4
13. (b) 3-point moving averages are: 275, 350, 425, 500, 575, 650, and 725 (P); 425, 450, 475, 500, 525, 550 and 575 (Q) (d) May/August 1972 (e) Firm Q: much greater deviation from the moving average (f) £950

Exercise 9

1. £59.10
2. 2.3

3. 100; 119.0
4. For X: crude death-rate $= 14.8$, standardized death-rate $= 20.1$; for Y: crude death-rate $= 11.0$, standardized death-rate $= 20.9$
5. £12.19, £12.56, £12.31, and £12.56
6. (a) 90.9 and 122.7 (b) 74.1 and 81.5
7. (a) 17.0 (b) 3700, 83 000, 10 000, 10 800, 12 500, 12 200, 12 000, and 10 500 (c) 21.2
8. £54
9. 128.6
10. 103.2
11. D
12. C
13. 229
14. (b) 27, 7.7, 12, 26, and 105; 29.5
15. 116
16. 120, 125, and 110
17. 99
18. $47\frac{1}{2}$p

Exercise 10

1. (a) 210 (b) 3360 (c) 2730; $\frac{1}{35}$
2. (a) 15!/5! (b) $\frac{2}{3}$ (c) $\frac{1}{15}$ (d) $\frac{2}{21}$
3. (a) £23 (b) (i) $\frac{1}{2}$ (ii) $\frac{2}{9}$
4. (a) $\frac{1}{20}$ (b) $\frac{2}{5}$ (c) $\frac{11}{20}$
5. (a) (i) 12 (ii) 6 (iii) 6 (b) $\frac{1}{4}$
6. (a) 56 (b) (i) $\frac{1}{14}$ (ii) $\frac{3}{7}$
7. (a) $\frac{5}{36}$ (b) $\frac{13}{18}$ (c) $\frac{5}{18}$ (d) $\frac{7}{9}$
8. (a) 21; $\frac{1}{6}$ (b) $\frac{5}{6}$
9. (a) $2 \leq x \leq 10$; probabilities are $\frac{1}{24}, \frac{2}{24}, \frac{3}{24}, \frac{4}{24}, \frac{4}{24}, \frac{4}{24}, \frac{3}{24}, \frac{2}{24}$, and $\frac{1}{24}$ (b) 6; $\frac{25}{6}$
10. (a) (i) $\frac{16}{81}$ (ii) $\frac{8}{27}$ (b) $\frac{11}{30}$
11. (a) $\frac{5}{36}$ (b) $\frac{1}{16}$ (c) $\frac{25}{216}$ (d) $\frac{1291}{1296}$
12. (a) 1320; 56 (b) (i) $\binom{52}{4}$ (ii) $\frac{11}{4165}$ (iii) $13/\binom{52}{4}$ (iv) 24 (c) (i) $\frac{12}{51}$ (ii) $\frac{4}{51}$
13. (a) (i) 720 (ii) 120 (iii) 24; 15 (b) (i) 0.0225 (ii) 0.2112 (iii) 0.1536 (iv) 0.8649 (v) 0.024
14. $H^4 + 4H^3T + 6H^2T^2 + 4HT^3 + T^4$; (a) (i) $\frac{1}{16}$ (ii) $\frac{3}{8}$ (b) (i) $\frac{3}{4}$ (ii) $\frac{1}{4}$ (iii) $\frac{3}{64}$
15. (a) (i) $\frac{1}{27}$ (ii) $\frac{6}{27}$ (iii) $\frac{1}{9}$ (b) (i) $\frac{1}{1716}$ (ii) $\frac{1}{286}$
16. (a) 7 (There are more ways of combining the two dice to give this particular score.) (b) (i) $\frac{5}{24}$ (ii) $\frac{3}{4}$
18. (a) $\frac{8}{27}$ (b) $\frac{19}{27}$ (c) $\frac{20}{27}$
19. (a) $\frac{1}{3}$ (b) $\frac{4}{9}$
20. $\frac{169}{330}$
21. (a) $\frac{1}{36}, \frac{1}{18}, \frac{1}{12}, \frac{1}{9}, \frac{5}{36}, \frac{1}{6}, \frac{5}{36}, \frac{1}{9}, \frac{1}{12}, \frac{1}{18}$, and $\frac{1}{36}$ (b) 7 (c) $\frac{1}{81}$ (d) $\frac{125}{216}$ (e) 15 (f) Expected frequencies are 2, 4, 6, 8, 10, 12, 10, 8, 6, 4, and 2 (for scores of 2, 3, 4 etc.); one die always produces a six while the other is unbiased.
22. (a) (i) 20 (ii) $\frac{9}{100}$ (iii) $\frac{3}{25}$ (iv) $\frac{27}{100}$ (b) (i) 20 (ii) $\frac{1}{15}$ (iii) $\frac{2}{15}$ (iv) $\frac{4}{15}$.

Stafford College

Exercise 11

1. (a) $25.8 \to 26.2$ cm (b) $331 \to 345$ cm^3
2. $1.95 \to 2.29$
3. A
4. B
5. $24.8 \to 24.9$
6. $1.166 \to 1.171$
7. (a) -0.042 (b) -0.0134 (c) -1.34 per cent
8. $41 \to 45$
9. $6.8 \to 7.9$
10. (a) $21.5 \to 23.49$ cm (b) $21.95 \to 23.949$ cm
11. $49.0 \to 51.0$ km/h
12. 8.55
14. (a) 27 400 (b) 26 700 (c) unbiased: $+0.462$ per cent, biased: -2.11 per cent
15. 4.8 tonnes; $+8.3$ per cent
16. 740 m $\to$ 820 m gallons
17. (a) 14.02, 13.98 (b) 10.035, 9.965; 0.0025; 0.02
18. 5.88 and 6.12 m/s
19. (a) 142 m (b) 1165 m^2
20. (a) 5 (b) 0.5

Exercise 12

1. $1.5 \times (0.9)^5$
2. (a) 5 (b) 30 (c) 75 (d) 110
3. (a) 10^{-5}, (b) 7.29×10^{-2}
4. (a) $\frac{1024}{3125}$ (b) $\frac{181}{3125}$
5. (a) $\frac{47}{128}$ (b) 50 (c) $5\sqrt{6}/2[6.12]$
6. (a) $\frac{59\,049}{100\,000}$ (b) $\frac{729}{10\,000}$ (c) $\frac{107}{12\,500}$
7. 5
8. (a) 3 (b) $\frac{7}{3}$
9. C
10. (a) 2.29 (b) 1.43
11. (a) 2 (b) 52 (c) 50 (d) 0.0228
12. (a) 26 (b) 47 (c) 0.7225
13. (b) 0.6826, 0.9544, and 0.9973 (c) (i) 74 (ii) 10
14. (a) 0.0548 (b) 2.3 (c) 0.5762
15. $\simeq 2$ per cent
16. (b) 0.53 (c) 23.5
17. (a) 1.24 (b) 2.42; 1.505 cm
18. $\mu = 1.68$ and $\sigma = 0.09$; 0.13
19. (a) $\frac{16}{25}$ (b) $\frac{48}{125}$: 0.017
20. (a) 0.263 (b) $\simeq 0.006$
21. (a) 320 and 8 (b) $\frac{309}{3125}$
22. $\frac{4}{5}$; (a) 0.106 (b) 0.33

23. (a) $\mu = 16$ and $\sigma = 3.67$ (b) 0.98

24. (a) $1.96 \rightarrow 2.84$ (b) $1.76 \rightarrow 3.04$

25. μ and σ^2/n; yes, '101' differs from the mean by 3.33 standard deviations; 3600

26. Actual values: 71.6 and 1.8; predicted values: 70.6 and 1.9; the agreement is bound to be imperfect, firstly because class marks are not necessarily the true mean for each class, and secondly because only a small number of sample-means was considered. Bearing all this in mind the agreement is surprisingly good!

27. (a) 805.8 and 0.5275 (b) $804.8 \rightarrow 806.8$

28. (a) Mean $= 9$ and standard deviation $= 2.6$ (b) Taking '14' as '13.5 $\rightarrow$ 14.5,' and using the lower limit of 13.5 we get $z = 1.73$. Therefore, using a one-tailed test, there is improvement at the 5 per cent level $(z < 1.64)$.

29. 0.29; $100.0 \rightarrow z = 3.33$, therefore, using a one-tailed test, significant result at both 5 per cent $(z < 1.64)$ and 1 per cent $(z < 2.33)$ levels.

30. (a) (i) 0.106 (ii) 0.478 (b) '50' $\rightarrow z = 2.34$, therefore, using a two-tailed test, significant result at 5 per cent $(z = 1.96)$ but not 1 per cent $(z = 2.58)$.

Appendix

Derivation of an alternative form of the standard deviation

$$s = \sqrt{\frac{\sum fd^2}{\sum f}}$$

$$= \sqrt{\frac{\sum f(x - \bar{x})^2}{\sum f}}$$

$$= \sqrt{\frac{\sum f(x^2 - 2x\bar{x} + \bar{x}^2)}{\sum f}}$$

$$= \sqrt{\frac{\sum fx^2 - \sum 2fx\bar{x} + \sum f\bar{x}^2}{\sum f}}$$

$$= \sqrt{\frac{\sum fx^2}{\sum f} - \frac{2\bar{x}\sum fx}{\sum f} + \frac{\bar{x}^2\sum f}{\sum f}}$$

and since $\dfrac{\sum fx}{\sum f} = \bar{x}$, we get

$$s = \sqrt{\frac{\sum fx^2}{\sum f} - 2\bar{x}^2 + \bar{x}^2}$$

$$= \sqrt{\frac{\sum fx^2}{\sum f} - \bar{x}^2}$$

This last formula, which can be taken as $s = \sqrt{\dfrac{\sum fx^2}{\sum f} - (\text{mean})^2}$; enables the

S.D. to be found without calculating any deviations at all. It is especially useful if the xs are *small*. If the xs are large it is still useful, providing an electronic calculator is available.

Proof of the coding formula for the standard deviation
We have to prove that the true standard deviation, $s = cs'$, where s' is the coded standard deviation and c is the class width: i.e. we have to prove that:

$$s = c\sqrt{\frac{\sum f(x')^2}{\sum f} - \left(\frac{\sum fx'}{\sum f}\right)^2} \qquad (1)$$

$$\left[\text{where } s = \sqrt{\frac{\sum fx^2}{\sum f} - \left(\frac{\sum fx}{\sum f}\right)^2}\right]$$

Proof

$$x' = \frac{(x - a)}{c}$$

Therefore right-hand side of equation (1)

$$= c\sqrt{\frac{\sum f(x - a)^2/c^2}{\sum f} - \left(\frac{\sum f(x - a)/c}{\sum f}\right)^2}$$

$$= c\sqrt{\frac{\sum fx^2 - \sum 2fax + \sum fa^2}{c^2\sum f} - \frac{(\sum fx - \sum fa)^2}{(c\sum f)^2}}$$

$$= c\sqrt{\frac{\sum fx^2 - 2a\sum fx + a^2\sum f}{c^2\sum f} - \left[\frac{(\sum fx)^2 - 2a\sum f\cdot\sum fx + a^2(\sum f)^2}{c^2(\sum f)^2}\right]}$$

$$= c\sqrt{\frac{\sum f\cdot\sum fx^2 - 2a\sum f\cdot\sum fx + a^2(\sum f)^2 - (\sum fx)^2 + 2a\sum f\cdot\sum fx - a^2(\sum f)^2}{c^2(\sum f)^2}}$$

$$= \sqrt{\frac{\sum f\cdot\sum fx^2 - (\sum fx)^2}{(\sum f)^2}}$$

$$= \sqrt{\frac{\sum f\sum fx^2}{(\sum f)^2} - \frac{(\sum fx)^2}{(\sum f)^2}}$$

$$= \sqrt{\frac{\sum fx^2}{\sum f} - \left(\frac{\sum fx}{\sum f}\right)^2}$$

$= s$

= left-hand side of equation (1)

i.e. right-hand side = left-hand side
Equation (1) is thus proved.

The Product-moment correlation coefficient

We have two formulae for the product-moment linear correlation coefficient
(r) which, for a set of $n(x, y)$ values are

$$r = \frac{\sum(x - \bar{x})\cdot(y - \bar{y})}{\sqrt{\{\sum(x - \bar{x})^2 \cdot \sum(y - \bar{y})^2\}}} \tag{1}$$

and

$$r = \frac{\sum xy - (\sum x \sum y)/n}{\sqrt{\left\{\left[\sum x^2 - \frac{(\sum x)^2}{n}\right]\left[\sum y^2 - \frac{(\sum y)^2}{n}\right]\right\}}} \tag{2}$$

The equivalence of these two formulae can be demonstrated as follows:

$$\frac{\sum(x - \bar{x})\cdot(y - \bar{y})}{\sqrt{\{\sum(x - \bar{x})^2 \cdot \sum(y - \bar{y})^2\}}} = \frac{\dfrac{\sum(x - \bar{x})\cdot(y - \bar{y})}{n}}{\sqrt{\left\{\dfrac{\sum(x - \bar{x})^2}{n} \cdot \dfrac{\sum(y - \bar{y})^2}{n}\right\}}} \tag{3}$$

The *numerator* of the right-hand side of (3) is $\dfrac{\sum xy}{n} - \dfrac{\sum \bar{y}x}{n} - \dfrac{\sum \bar{x}y}{n} + \dfrac{\sum \bar{x}\bar{y}}{n}$

$$= \frac{\sum xy}{n} - \bar{y}\cdot\frac{\sum x}{n} - \bar{x}\cdot\frac{\sum y}{n} + \bar{x}\bar{y}\cdot\frac{\sum 1}{n}$$

$$= \frac{\sum xy}{n} - \bar{y}\bar{x} - \bar{x}\bar{y} + \bar{x}\bar{y}\cdot\frac{n}{n}$$

$$= \frac{\sum xy}{n} - \bar{x}\bar{y};$$

however, $\bar{x} = \dfrac{\sum x}{n}$ and $\bar{y} = \dfrac{\sum y}{n}$, so:

$$\text{numerator} = \frac{\sum xy}{n} - \frac{\sum x \cdot \sum y}{n^2};$$

it follows that:

$$\sum(x - \bar{x})(y - \bar{y}) = \sum xy - \frac{\sum x \cdot \sum y}{n}$$

Additionally, the first expression in the *denominator* of the right-hand side of (3) is

$$\sqrt{\frac{\sum x^2}{n} - \frac{\sum 2\bar{x}x}{n} + \frac{\sum \bar{x}^2}{n}}$$

$$= \sqrt{\frac{\sum x^2}{n} - 2\bar{x}\frac{\sum x}{n} + \bar{x}^2\frac{\sum 1}{n}}$$

$$= \sqrt{\frac{\sum x^2}{n} - 2\frac{(\sum x)^2}{n^2} + \frac{(\sum x)^2}{n^2}}$$

So the first expression in the denominator of (3) is

$$\sqrt{\frac{\sum x^2}{n} - \frac{(\sum x)^2}{n^2}} \; ;$$

it follows that

$$\sqrt{\sum(x - \bar{x})^2} = \sqrt{\sum x^2 - \frac{(\sum x)^2}{n}}$$

And in a precisely similar fashion

$$\sqrt{\sum(y - \bar{y})^2} = \sqrt{\sum y^2 - \frac{(\sum y)^2}{n}}$$

Accordingly:

$$\text{Formula (1)} = \text{Formula (2)}.$$

To prove that the mean or expected value of the binomial distribution is np
For a discrete or Grouped Frequency Distribution we have already shown that the mean, $\bar{x}$, is given by the following:

$$\bar{x} = \frac{\sum fx}{\sum f}. \tag{1}$$

Now, equation (1) can be written in full as:

$$\bar{x} = \frac{f_1 x_1 + f_2 x_2 + f_3 x_3 + \ldots + f_n x_n}{\sum f}$$

or

$$\bar{x} = \frac{f_1}{\sum f} \cdot x_1 + \frac{f_2}{\sum f} \cdot x_2 + \frac{f_3}{\sum f} \cdot x_3 + \ldots + \frac{f_n}{\sum f} \cdot x_n \tag{2}$$

However, $\dfrac{f_1}{\sum f}, \dfrac{f_2}{\sum f}$, etc. are *relative* frequencies or *probabilities* so equation (2) transforms to:

$$\bar{x} = p_1 x_1 + p_2 x_2 + p_3 x_3 + \ldots + p_n x_n$$

i.e.

$$\bar{x} = \sum px$$

For the binomial distribution,

$$p(x) = \binom{n}{x} p^x q^{n-x}$$

and so

$$\bar{x} = \sum px$$
$$= \sum \binom{n}{x} p^x q^{n-x} x$$
$$= \sum \frac{n!}{x!(n-x)!} p^x q^{n-x} x$$

$$= \sum \frac{n!}{(x-1)!(n-x)!} p^x q^{n-x}$$

$$= np \sum \frac{(n-1)!}{(x-1)!(n-x)!} p^{x-1} q^{n-x}$$

$$= np \sum \binom{n-1}{x-1} p^{x-1} q^{n-x}$$

$$= np(p+q)^{n-1}$$

However, $p + q = 1$, so

$$\bar{x} = np \cdot 1$$

$$= np$$

$$\Rightarrow \bar{x} = np$$

To prove that the variance of the binomial distribution is npq or np(1 − p)
The variance, s^2, of a discrete or Grouped Frequency Distribution has previously been shown to be:

$$s^2 = \frac{\sum fx^2}{\sum f} - \bar{x}^2 \tag{3}$$

So in relative frequency or probability terms (see Section 12.2.1) equation (3) can be transformed to:

$$s^2 = \sum px^2 - \bar{x}^2$$

For the binomial distribution,

$$p(x) = \binom{n}{x} p^x q^{n-x}$$

and so:

$$s^2 = \sum px^2 - \bar{x}^2$$

$$= \sum \binom{n}{x} p^x q^{n-x} x^2 - \bar{x}^2$$

$$= \sum [x(x-1) + x] \binom{n}{x} p^x q^{n-x} - \bar{x}^2$$

$$= \sum x(x-1) \binom{n}{x} p^x q^{n-x} + \sum \binom{n}{x} p^x q^{n-x} x - \bar{x}^2$$

$$= \sum \frac{x(x-1)n!}{x!(n-x)!} p^x \cdot q^{n-x} + \bar{x} - \bar{x}^2$$

$$= n(n-1)p^2 \sum \frac{(n-2)!}{(x-2)!(n-x)!} p^{x-2} q^{n-x} + \bar{x} - \bar{x}^2$$

$$= n(n-1)p^2(p+q)^{n-2} + \bar{x} - \bar{x}^2$$

However, $p + q = 1$ and $\bar{x} = np$, so

$$s^2 = n(n-1)p^2 1^{n-2} + np - n^2 p^2$$

$$\Rightarrow s^2 = n^2 p^2 - np^2 + np - n^2 p^2$$

i.e. $$s^2 = np(1 - p) \tag{4}$$

Since $p + q = 1$, however, $q = 1 - p$, so equation (4) can also be written as:

$$s^2 = npq$$

and this expression is somewhat easier to commit to memory.

The integral, P, of the normal probability function

X	.00	.01	.02	.03	.04	.05	.06	.07	.08	.09
.0	.5000	.5040	.5080	.5120	.5160	.5199	.5239	.5279	.5319	.5359
.1	.5398	.5438	.5478	.5517	.5557	.5596	.5636	.5675	.5714	.5753
.2	.5793	.5832	.5871	.5910	.5948	.5987	.6026	.6064	.6103	.6141
.3	.6179	.6217	.6255	.6293	.6331	.6368	.6406	.6443	.6480	.6517
.4	.6554	.6591	.6628	.6664	.6700	.6736	.6772	.6808	.6844	.6879
.5	.6915	.6950	.6985	.7019	.7054	.7088	.7123	.7157	.7190	.7224
.6	.7257	.7291	.7324	.7357	.7389	.7422	.7454	.7486	.7517	.7549
.7	.7580	.7611	.7642	.7673	.7704	.7734	.7764	.7794	.7823	.7852
.8	.7881	.7910	.7939	.7967	.7995	.8023	.8051	.8078	.8106	.8133
.9	.8159	.8186	.8212	.8238	.8264	.8289	.8315	.8340	.8365	.8389
1.0	.8413	.8438	.8461	.8485	.8508	.8531	.8554	.8577	.8599	.8621
1.1	.8643	.8665	.8686	.8708	.8729	.8749	.8770	.8790	.8810	.8830
1.2	.8849	.8869	.8888	.8907	.8925	.8944	.8962	.8980	.8997	.9015
1.3	.9032	.9049	.9066	.9082	.9099	.9115	.9131	.9147	.9162	.9177
1.4	.9192	.9207	.9222	.9236	.9251	.9265	.9279	.9292	.9306	.9319
1.5	.9332	.9345	.9357	.9370	.9382	.9394	.9406	.9418	.9429	.9441
1.6	.9452	.9463	.9474	.9484	.9495	.9505	.9515	.9525	.9535	.9545
1.7	.9554	.9564	.9573	.9582	.9591	.9599	.9608	.9616	.9625	.9633
1.8	.9641	.9649	.9656	.9664	.9671	.9678	.9686	.9693	.9699	.9706
1.9	.9713	.9719	.9726	.9732	.9738	.9744	.9750	.9756	.9761	.9767

X	.00	.01	.02	.03	.04	.05	.06	.07	.08	.09
2.0	.9772	.9778	.9783	.9788	.9793	.9798	.9803	.9808	.9812	.9817
2.1	.9821	.9826	.9830	.9834	.9838	.9842	.9846	.9850	.9854	.9857
2.2	.9861	.9864	.9868	.9871	.9875	.9878	.9881	.9884	.9887	.9890
2.3	.9893	.9896	.9898	.99010	.99036	.99061	.99086	.99111	.99134	.99158
2.4	.99180	.99202	.99224	.99245	.99266	.99286	.99305	.99324	.99343	.99361
2.5	.99379	.99396	.99413	.99430	.99446	.99461	.99477	.99492	.99506	.99520
2.6	.99534	.99547	.99560	.99573	.99585	.99598	.99609	.99621	.99632	.99643
2.7	.99653	.99664	.99674	.99683	.99693	.99702	.99711	.99720	.99728	.99736
2.8	.99744	.99752	.99760	.99767	.99774	.99781	.99788	.99795	.99801	.99807
2.9	.99813	.99819	.99825	.99831	.99836	.99841	.99846	.99851	.99856	.99861

Linear interpolation sufficient

X	3.0	3.1	3.2	3.3	3.4	3.5	3.6	3.7	3.8	3.9
P	.99865	.99903	.99931	.99952	.99966	.99977	.99984	.99980	.99993	.99995
Z	.00443	.00327	.00238	.00172	.00123	.00087	.00061	.00042	.00029	.00020

$$P = \frac{1}{\sqrt{2\pi}} \int_{-\infty}^{X} e^{-(1/2)X^2}\,dx, \quad Z = \frac{1}{\sqrt{2\pi}} e^{-(1/2)X^2}$$

X is the standardized variable with zero mean and unit standard deviation.
For negative values of X note: $P(X) = 1 - P(-X)$

RANDOM SAMPLING NUMBERS

9580	5824	5290	8129	1613	3215	6568	5837	0755	1057
7489	0643	3085	4434	7814	7969	2708	2543	8381	5418
9305	2831	1219	3558	9905	2540	4905	8613	1913	3851
0114	0178	2633	0487	3572	9195	5267	6254	2830	8204
4857	6761	1469	7227	1956	4066	9802	0212	4792	4264
5610	6556	6734	5055	3249	3826	1698	7058	5498	3934
0594	5778	2766	5802	0923	3869	6404	6169	2979	3988
2510	2505	9602	6451	5587	9279	0359	9012	8772	1478
0455	6388	3397	4400	9027	3331	1329	3357	6298	1675
4460	6888	2592	9598	0446	0626	2807	5231	8343	0209
3574	0962	6806	8134	4569	6243	1468	9966	8270	4659
8893	9929	5718	3408	6100	4856	2204	3334	2281	9455
3460	4196	4445	1833	2947	3620	0536	7798	1460	1551
6723	3763	3185	5019	3081	6605	2401	9927	2339	6672
9619	0159	8410	8703	5235	4671	2326	4808	1559	0117
3660	9123	2061	1576	2930	5598	9051	8392	5096	3226
0905	9754	7534	9879	2883	4400	8532	1483	0081	6957
6261	5621	7807	5058	0451	5195	3276	3896	7046	0587
9184	1230	3265	7708	1739	5697	6500	2579	6172	8171
2273	9063	2033	0272	9936	3285	7531	7206	4679	1484
3573	4520	1440	8721	5873	8892	8769	9801	6249	8774
6545	5008	3761	1428	9967	0909	1126	4889	8618	2608
9293	0179	1531	2586	2177	1789	0581	0946	6947	5286
9088	8636	5854	5947	3022	6938	8655	4295	4743	1135
7784	7318	6422	4825	1554	0570	7897	0503	6710	4947

5424	9638	9645	7864	6322	4546	6519	8667	0811	9705
9625	4744	3447	5288	3958	7685	1894	0478	2801	7203
0460	8491	3230	4472	0029	8220	0871	6645	7002	9373
9522	5421	9882	0664	5823	6727	3790	3910	4155	6823
9221	8964	7744	9890	9359	7105	7947	6626	7214	3056
8505	9526	5649	9260	7104	6368	0015	7477	2390	0033
3847	1445	9926	9622	4250	6822	1224	4916	1860	7671
7299	4290	9502	6991	6466	6098	5481	6295	1386	6554
8361	2080	2094	3145	2326	8381	6392	1203	4795	5201
6783	5993	2106	3159	1451	5522	7924	6846	5999	5729
1175	1610	9178	4061	1682	9740	0357	8010	7549	3187
6218	9780	6888	0852	0703	0417	4045	2575	9318	9226
3366	6764	9347	7652	8072	2148	4296	4091	4156	1200
6633	2308	3655	5023	8034	2093	3089	5003	7250	0593
5160	1508	2759	8586	4000	3788	6728	0865	8687	7202
6293	9102	4365	8637	3919	9417	8409	5696	6298	7294
1425	7260	4143	4485	4027	9776	4414	5669	1309	7619
6526	7388	8651	8126	2191	7116	0361	8865	8428	8122
0222	7173	4156	9180	3965	4382	0783	5038	5722	3798
					1444	4411	3160	9156	2301
					3382	8520	3422	7648	8097
					9538	2049	6992	9302	9689

Index